Acknowledgement
Much as we would like to claim the idea for this book we must
acknowledge that it stems from a range of publications published in
Australia by Tom and Wendy Whitton of Second Back Row Press,
Sydney. This book is published with their blessing and we hope it
measures up to the standards that they set.

The first edition of **Bookshops of London** was researched and
written by Diana Stephenson who also updated the next three
editions. Much of the research work for the fifth edition was
undertaken by Anthony Taylor. This sixth edition, expanded to
cover the entire county of Greater London was researched and
edited by R.J. Thomas to whom acknowledgement is gratefully
given.

Improvements
While every effort has been made to give accurate information and
descriptions of the shops listed, we must disclaim responsibility for
any errors.

We welcome written information or suggestions which might
make the next edition even better.

We have tried to include all shops retailing books. If we have
omitted any, please let us know. Note the paragraph on
'Exclusions' before doing so.

BOOKSHOPS
of GREATER
LONDON

Roger Lascelles, Cartographic and Travel Publisher
47 York Road, Brentford, Middlesex TW8 OQP Telephone: 081-847 0935

Messages from the Publisher

To Bookshop Owners and Managers

Keeping tabs on nearly 800 bookshops in a city the size of Greater London is no sinecure. We will be keeping a correction copy of this edition and entering fresh information as it reaches us.

We invite you to check your entries and to pass any corrections/criticisms to us.

It is easy enough to adjust trading hours and changes to telephone number or address. As to subjects handled we do not care to list all categories handled by a 'general' bookshop, but we are especially interested in those subjects which are handled with some degree of specialisation. If you reckon to have a better than average collection of books on any particular subject or subjects, then we invite you to let us know (in writing) and we will lodge your advice in our 'title file' for attention when revision work for the next edition commences.

To Publishers' Representatives

One self-important publisher told us that he had been selling books for over 20 years and knew all there was to know about London Bookshops.

If he had coped with the flood of changes with which we had to deal in preparing for this edition, we venture to suggest he would have piped a very different tune. For in truth the world of bookselling — in London at least — is highly organic. New seeds are planted and old plants die. Some firms contract, others expand — sometimes with branches — while some move. Telephone numbers are altered, hours of trade adjusted and premises developed. The changes are endless.

The harried and conscientious publisher's representative has been unable to keep up with all of these changes — until now! We created this book initially to help our own London representatives, but with the idea that if it could be developed suitably, it would be invaluable to those of other publishers. A good representative knows all the bookshops in his or her territory even though he or she may not regularly call on them all.

This book enables the representative to know some of the shops without having to call on them. If for example he or she is selling history books, it is a waste of time to call on specialists in witchcraft, dentistry or gastronomy.

To Marketing and Sales Directors in Publishing

You probably know quite a bit about a clutch of London shops, but as to the newer ones, you could well have some doubts.

If the battle commander lacks field intelligence, how can he direct the front line troops?

We hope that this book will be of particular help to you when discussing calling schedules and territory changes.

Explanations

Sequence Adopted. Shops have been grouped by postal district and are in fact listed in post code order. This has been done largely for the convenience of publishers and their representatives — amongst the principal users of this book.

Shop Index. The alphabetical shop index will assist those readers who may not know the postal district system of London.

Subject Index. Booksellers with any degree of specialisation are listed by number in the Subject Index which will be found at the back of the book.

Exclusions. This book does not include bookshops specialising in pornography, nor does it include newsagents whose stock is non-book by nature. We have also excluded minor shops of the major chains as these also are principally retailers of the magazines and stationery.

Dealers in books who are not retailers to the public have also been excluded as have those retailers who are open only on two or three days a week.

Publication Data

Title	Bookshops of Greater London
Typeface	Phototypeset in Compugraphic Times
Printing	Kelso Graphics, Kelso, Scotland.
ISBN	0 903909 82 0
Edition	First, Oct 1981. Second Feb 1982. Third, Jul 1984. Fourth, Jun 1985. Fifth, Jul 1986. Sixth, Mar 1990.
Publisher	Roger Lascelles 47 York Road, Brentford, Middlesex, TW8 0QP.
Copyright	Roger Lascelles

Distribution

Africa:	South Africa —	Faradawn, Box 17161, Hillbrow 2038
Americas:	Canada —	International Travel Maps & Books, P.O. Box 2290, Vancouver BC V6B 3W5
	U.S.A. —	Boerum Hill Books, P.O. Box 286, Times Plaza Station, Brooklyn, NY 11217, (718-624-4000).
Asia:	India —	English Book Store, 17-L Connaught Circus/P.O. Box 328, New Delhi 110 001
	Singapore —	Graham Brash Pte Ltd., 36-C Prinsep St
Australasia:	Australia —	Rex Publications, 413 Pacific Highway, Artarmon NSW 2064. 428 3566
Europe:	Belgium —	Brussels - Peuples et Continents
	Germany —	Available through major booksellers with good foreign travel sections
	GB/Ireland —	Available through all booksellers with good foreign travel sections
	Italy —	Libreria dell'Automobile, Milano
	Netherlands —	Nilsson & Lamm BV, Weesp
	Denmark —	Copenhagen - Arnold Busck, G.E.C. Gad, Boghallen, G.E.C. Gad
	Finland —	Helsinki — Akateeminen Kirjakauppa
	Norway —	Oslo - Arne Gimnes/J.G. Tanum
	Sweden —	Stockholm/Esselte, Akademi Bokhandel, Fritzes, Hedengrens Gothenburg/Gumperts, Esselte Lund/Gleerupska
	Switzerland —	Basel/Bider: Berne/Atlas; Geneve/Artou; Lausanne/Artou: Zurich/Travel Bookshop

Contents

EAST END BOOKSHOP
Tower Hamlets Arts Project Books Ltd.
178 Whitechapel, London E1 1BJ.   **071-247 0216**

Subjects: General, local history, bi-lingual books, especially
                Bengali, children's books.
Hours: Tue - Fri 10.00 - 5.30. Sat 10.00 - 5.00.
Services: Savings cards. Bookstalls in local schools and colleges.
                Educational and library supply.

Great enthusiasm and initiative started this community bookshop in
Tower Hamlets and continues today. Vivid colours attract the eye
and apart from the general stock they specialise in the history of the
East End. Their children's section is very important and they have
a policy of not stocking sexist or racist books and reach schools and
colleges with their bookstall system. Savings cards enable the
children with little money to save for a chosen book. The bi-lingual
section is a great asset to the Bengali community, also specialist
books for adult literary courses and help and advice for the local
inhabitant is always on hand.

The bookshop is moving early in 1990 to larger premises near
Whitechapel tube station. Once there, they will also be selling
educational toys and games and holding book events such as author
signings, storytelling for children, and writers' workshops. They
intend to build up a stock of secondhand books on East London.

QUEEN MARY COLLEGE BOOKSHOP
Queen Mary College, Mile End Road,
London E1 4NS.   **081-980 2554**

Subjects: Biology, chemistry, computer science, engineering
                (aeronautical, civil, electrical, mechanical), materials
                science, mathematics, physics, fiction.
Hours: Mon - Fri 9.00 - 5.30. Wed 9.00 - 4.30.
Services: Account facilities, mail order, special orders, credit cards.
On the ground floor of the main campus building, this large and
recently refurbished bookshop carries a wide range of student texts
as well as a lively fiction section and a good selection of stationery
products. Helpful staff are always ready to take special orders.

THE LONDON YACHT CENTRE LTD.
13 Artillery Lane, London E1 7LP.   **071-247 0521**

Subjects: Sailing.
Hours: Mon - Fri 9.00 - 5.30. Thu 9.30 - 7.00 (March - Aug)
Services: Credit cards, special orders.

A small department at the Yacht Centre is allocated to books for 'the sailor'. Yachtsmen's charts, books on navigation and the practical side of sailing are stocked. Special orders taken.

ZWEMMER'S AT THE WHITECHAPEL GALLERY
80 Whitechapel High Street, London E1 7QX.   **071-247 6924**

Subjects: Twentieth century art, architecture, photography and design.
Hours: Tue - Sun 11.00 - 5.00. Wed 11.00 - 8.00.
Services: Special orders, mail order, credit cards.

This branch of Zwemmer's inside the Whitechapel Art Gallery stocks a wide range of books on twentieth century art and architecture, both foreign and English. It also stocks background books to the current exhibitions at the gallery itself, as well as current exhibition catalogues from elsewhere. Comprehensive selections of postcards and art magazines and some posters are also available.

FREEDOM BOOKSHOP
84b Whitechapel High Street,
(Angel Alley), London E1 7QX   **071-247 9249**

Subjects: Anarchist politics.
Hours: Mon - Fri 10.00 - 6.00. Sat 10.00 - 4.00.
Services: Mail order, catalogue, special orders.

Freedom Press have their offices here, at the bottom of an alley near the Whitechapel Art Gallery. On the first floor the public are welcome to purchase books, pamphlets and magazines on anarchist politics.

THE LONDON BUDDHIST CENTRE BOOKSHOP
51 Roman Road,   **081-981 1225**
London E2 0HU   **081-980 4391**

Subjects: Buddhism, health.
Hours: Mon - Fri 10.00 - 5.00.
Services: Special orders, mail order, catalogue (send large SAE), LBC tape library, book tokens.

This small bookshop within the London Buddhist Centre stocks the canonical Buddhist texts in English translation, works from the Zen, Mahayana and Tibetan schools, and general, biographical, historical and philosophical books on Buddhism. An associated enterprise, Dharmachakra Tapes, distributes lectures by the Ven. Sangharakshita, founder of the Centre. These, as well as all his written works, are available from the bookshop. A large range of candles, incense, devotional objects, meditation stools and cushions is also stocked.

JAMBALA BOOKSHOP
247 Globe Road, Bethnal Green, London E2 0JD. 081-981 4037

Subjects: Mind and body, ecology, children's, vegetarian cookery.
Hours: Mon - Wed, Fri 11.00 - 6.00. Thu 12.00 - 6.00. Sat 10.00 - 6.00.
Services: Special orders.

Opened in June 1988, Jambala Bookshop has built up a reputation for friendly service. The business is run by Buddhists as a co-operative.

HUNGARIAN BOOK AGENCY
**87 Sewardstone Road, Victoria Park,
Bethnal Green, London E2 9HN.   081-980 9096**

Subjects: Hungarian literature, art, music, periodicals.
Hours: Thu - Sat 11.00 - 5.00. Other times by appointment.
Services: Mail order.

This shop, previously known as the Danubia Book Company, is mainly a mail order business but is open to the public three days a week. Visitors are welcome outside these hours by appointment. As well as books in Hungarian on most subjects, there is a good selection of books in English about Hungary. Mail orders are dispatched within twenty-four hours and subscriptions arranged immediately.

THE BARGAIN BOOKSHOP
135 Station Road, North Chingford,
London E4 6AG.   **081-524 9002**

Subjects: Remainders.
Hours: Mon - Sat 9.30 - 5.30.
Services: Special orders (including full-price books), out of print
book search, book tokens, credit cards.

A small family-run shop near Chingford railway station, with the emphasis on personal service. All the remainders, paperback and hardback, are available at under half the previously published price.

VILLAGE ARCADE BOOKSHOP
8 Village Arcade, Station Road,
Chingford, London E4 7BJ.   **081-524 9235**

Subjects: General.
Hours: Mon - Sat 9.00 - 5.00.
Services: Special orders, book tokens, credit cards.

A small shop in an attractive Victorian arcade with a large selection of bestsellers in hardback and paperback. Attention is paid to individual requirements.

W.H. SMITH LTD.
125 High Street North, London E6 1HZ.   **081-552 4875/6**

Subjects: General.
Hours: Mon - Sat 9.00 - 6.00.
Services: Special orders, credit cards.

A long shop, shelving books under subject headings with a corner for children's books. There is a permanent table top display of remaindered and bargain books.

THE COLLEGE BOOKSHOP
Newham Community College, East Ham Centre,
High Street South, East Ham, London E6 4ER.   **081-472 9946**

Subjects: Academic.
Hours: Day: Mon - Fri 9.00 - 3.00. Evening: Mon - Thu 6.00 - 8.00. (Termtime only).
Services: Special orders.

This bookshop serves the students of the college and stocks only books which are used by them. Students from other colleges are welcome to purchase books and special orders are dealt with promptly. Newham Community College was formerly known as East Ham Technical College.

ROUND ABOUT BOOKS
368 Mare Street, London E8 1HR.   **081-985 8148**

Subjects: General.
Hours: Mon - Sat 8.00 - 6.00
Services: Special orders.

Firstly a functioning newsagent but with a good stock of general reference, fiction and leisure reading. The section on local history is their speciality.

CENTERPRISE BOOKSHOP
136-138 Kingsland High Street,
Hackney, London E8 2NS.   **071-254 9632/5**

Subjects: General, feminist, radical, Black culture, children's.
Hours: Tue - Sat 10.30 - 5.30.
Services: Special orders, school library supply.

This is a community bookshop with a coffee and snack bar
attached. The emphasis is on multi-racial, non-sexist and working
class books. The shop also stocks its own publications of local
interest as well as those of other small publishing houses.

DITCHFIELDS
790-794 High Road, Leyton, London E10 6AE.   **081-539 2821**

Subjects: General.
Hours: Mon - Sat 9.15 - 5.30 (Thu 9.15 - 1.00).

'Gifts for all occasions' is how Ditchfield's describe their stock.
Bicycles to porcelain — but with a small stock of books of general
appeal, maps and travel guides.

THE COMIC SHACK
720 High Road, Leytonstone,
London E11 3NN.   **081-539 7260**

Subjects: American comics, science fiction, horror, romance,
               French comics.
Hours: Mon - Thu 9.30 - 5.30. Fri, Sat 9.30 - 6.30.

The Comic Shack is opposite McDonalds and near the Green Man
Roundabout. They have fifty thousand American comics in stock
and thousands of science fiction paperbacks. Some hardback books
too.

NEWHAM PARENTS' CENTRE BOOKSHOP
Parents Centre Activities (Newham) Ltd.
745/747 Barking Road,
Plaistow, London E13 9ER.   **081-552 9993**

Subjects: General, educational, children's books and play
                materials, multi-ethnic, women's studies.
Hours: Mon - Fri 9.30 - 5.30. Wed 9.30 - 1.00. Sat 9.30 - 5.00.
Services: Special orders, school and college supply, newsletter.
                Reading help scheme.

This centre is a charity open to individuals and groups living or
working in Newham. Its aim is to seek out and publicise information
on education, therefore their stock of educational books is their
speciality. This includes reading schemes in schools, adult literacy
schemes and an excellent children's section. There is a Reading Help
Scheme backed by a mobile Education Shop which travels to
Dockland sites. Reference books have their section and the Arts
include East End Writings and Poetry. A most enterprising venture.

W.H. SMITH LTD.
The Stratford Centre,
41-42 The Mall, London E15 1XE.   **081-534 5955**

Subjects: General, cookery.
Hours: Mon - Fri 9.00 - 6.00. Sat 8.30 - 6.00.
Services: Credit cards, special orders.

Recently refurbished, this branch of Smiths is located in the new
shopping centre at Stratford. There is a general range of hard and
paper-backed books with cookery as the longest section. Medical
and technical books for students reflect the hospitals and colleges
hereabouts.

NORMAN LORD
3 Antique City Market, 98 Wood Street,
Walthamstow, London E17 3HX.   **081-520 4032**

Subjects: General secondhand and antiquarian.
Hours: Mon - Sat 10.00 - 5.00. Thu closed.
Services: Book search service, auctions attended, books bought.

About 3,000 collectables and readables attractively displayed and
shrewdly priced. Literature (first editions and others) and biography
particularly well represented; also travel, hobbies, natural history,
military and children's books.

PSYCHIC SENSE BOOKSHOP
1 Antique City Market, 98 Wood Street,
Walthamstow, London E17 3HX.   **081-520 4032**

Subjects: Psychic, occult, tarot, astrology.
Hours: Mon - Sat 9.15 - 5.15. Thu closed.
Services: Mail order, book search service, books bought.

At the entrance to Antique City Market, this small shop carries new
and secondhand books for readers and collectors in its specialist
field.

RAYMOND PORT
4 Antique City Market, 98 Wood Street,
Walthamstow, London E17 3HX.   **081-520 4032**

Subjects: General new and secondhand, literature, local history.
Hours: Mon - Sat 9.30 - 5.00. Thu closed.
Services: Special orders, book search service, books bought.

An attractive shop specializing in books on London, Walthamstow
and Essex, and literature, particularly works on or by William
Morris. There are also children's books, a small gay and feminist
section and a new speciality, Dr. Who. A chance exchange of three
Dr. Who books by a regular customer who had received them for
Christmas has led to the development of a major new line of
business. Raymond Port now stocks everything in print on Dr. Who

- books, new and secondhand, and magazines. Such is the popularity of this cult figure that Mr. Port took a group of his regular Whovians to see the stage play in Canterbury recently.

DAVID ELLIS
Sporting Bookshop, 13 Antique City Market,
98 Wood Street, London E17 3HX.   **081-520 4032**

Subjects: Sport, secondhand and antiquarian.
Hours: Mon - Sat 9.30 - 5.00. Thu closed.
Services: Wants lists.

This bookshop has a good selection of books on cricket with football and boxing following close behind and some books on most sports.

FANFARE BOOKCENTRE
2 Chingford Road, Bell Corner,
London E17 4PJ.   **081-527 0035 (3 lines)**

Subjects: General, college text books, computing, psychology, psychiatry.
Hours: Mon - Sat 10.00 - 5.00.
Services: College and library supply, special orders, credit cards.

This bookshop runs a service to supply students at Waltham Forest College, Redbridge and Havering Technical Colleges, and the Polytechnic of East London, which gives an idea of the academic books available. The psychology and psychiatry books are a particular speciality.

FANFARE BOOKCENTRE
257 High Street, Walthamstow, London E17 7BH.   **081-521 4781**

Subjects: General, children's.
Hours: Mon - Sat 9.00 - 5.00.
Services: Special orders, credit cards.

An offshoot of the previous bookshop, it stocks both fiction and non-fiction in hardback and paperback and has a large selection of children's books.

E. & R. ABBOT LTD.
135 George Lane, South Woodford,
London E18 1AN.   081-989 6164

Subjects: General.
Hours: Mon - Fri 9.00 - 5.30 (Thu & Sat 9.00 - 5.00).

A stationers with a well chosen selection of general books. Strong on gardening, educational, travel and maps.

DOVE BOOKS
82 High Road, South Woodford,
London E18 2NA.   081-530 4244

Subjects: Christian literature.
Hours: Mon - Sat 9.30 - 5.30. Closed Thu.
Services: Special orders, book agencies, R.E. schools supply.

A Christian bookshop, supported by the local churches, providing a complete range of books, music, magazines and cards for churchgoer and non-churchgoer alike. The staff are experienced and helpful. There is a full range of Bibles always in stock, an excellent children's section, Christian music, traditional and contemporary, and information and resource materials for teachers of religious education. There is also a large selection of greetings cards for all occasions, a small stationery section and craftware and gifts. A free delivery service is in operation for schools; church and book agencies are welcome.

DENNY'S BOOKSELLERS LTD.
121 Newgate Street, London EC1A 7AA.   **071-606 3202**

Subjects: General.
Hours: Mon - Fri 9.00 - 6.00.
Services: Special orders, credit cards.

CHRISTIAN LITERATURE CRUSADE BOOKSHOP
26-30 Holborn Viaduct,
London EC1A 2AQ.   **071-583 4835/4837**

Subjects: Christianity, books for Sunday schools, etc.
Hours: Mon - Fri 9.30 - 5.30. Thu 9.30 - 6.00. Sat 9.30 - 5.00.
Services: Mail order, 10% discount for Church bookstalls.

The shop is on Holborn Viaduct, next door to City Temple Church, and is part of the Evangelical movement. There is a large open shop at ground floor level selling Bibles and Christian books, including some in other European languages. On the lower sales floor are children's books, Sunday School teaching materials, records, cassettes and greetings cards.

DENNY'S BOOKSELLERS LTD.
2, 4 and 5 Carthusian Street, London EC1M 6ED.   **071-253 5421**

Subjects: Medical, technical, scientific and general.
Hours: Mon - Fri 9.00 - 6.00.
Services: Special orders. Computerised ordering. University, Polytechnic and Industry supply. Credit cards. Mail order.

Denny's are international booksellers and are located just one minute from the Barbican underground with other branches in the U.K. They are specialists in medical, technical and scientific books but also have a general section. They supply Universities, Polytechnics and industry worldwide. For their larger customers they offer a fully computerised service and are able to tailor any specialist requirements to suit a client's particular needs. A very professional company.

W.H. SMITH LTD.   **071-242 0535**
Holborn Circus, 124 Holborn, London EC1N 2TD.
                                    Travel Department **071-242 9826**

Subjects: General, Travel.
Hours: Mon - Fri 8.30 - 5.30. Sat closed.
Services: Credit cards, special orders.

Opened only in 1980 this large branch is rather good for travel books
because it has a travel department next door. The book section is at
the back of the ground floor and includes a large selection of
contemporary and popular fiction in paperback. The rest of the
shop sells magazines, toys, stationery and recorded music.

THE CITY UNIVERSITY BOOKSHOP
Northampton Square, London EC1V 0HB.   **071-608 0706**

Subjects: Computing, engineering (civil, control, electrical,
               mechanical), journalism, optometry, speech therapy.
Hours: Mon, Wed, Fri 9.00 - 5.00. Tue, Thu 9.00 - 6.00. (Term
               time).
Services: Accounts facilities, mail order, special orders, credit
               cards.

Recently relocated in more spacious premises near the main entrance
of the City University, the shop has a wide range of recommended
student texts as well as a lively fiction and travel section and a good
selection of stationery products. The welcoming and knowledgeable
staff pride themselves on their fast special order service.

GENESIS BOOKS
East West Centre, 188 Old Street,
London EC1V 9BP.   **071-250 1868**

Subjects: Mind, body, spirit, New Age, environment, alternative
               medicine, natural healing, macrobiotics, astrology.
Hours: Mon - Fri 11.30 - 7.00. Sat 11.00 - 3.00 (or later).
Services: Mail order, catalogue, magazine subscriptions.

The bookshop specialises in books on alternative medicine and
oblique ways to spiritual health, surprising in this hard-nosed area.
It is located in the East West Centre, a natural health centre, which
offers macrobiotic consultations, shiatsu massage and other

alternative therapies as well as courses on many aspects of natural health including cookery. These concerns are reflected in the book stock. Non-book material includes New Age cassettes and CDs, videos on yoga, relaxation etc., crystals and greetings cards. There is a macrobiotic restaurant on the ground floor.

MENCAP BOOKSHOP
**Royal Society for Mentally Handicapped
  Children and Adults,
117/123 Golden Lane, London EC1Y ORT.**   **071-253 9433**

Subjects: Mental handicap
Hours: Mon - Fri 9.00 - 5.30
Services: Lists, quarterly journal, mail order.

This is a bright and colourful shop selling gifts as well as books. Its books are for those helping with the care of the mentally handicapped and the books range through sex education to language stimulation.

BOUTLE AND KING
Pitch 59, Exmouth Market, London EC1.

Subjects: General, printing, architecture (secondhand and antiquarian).
Hours: Mon - Fri 8.00 - 4.00.
Services: Search service, books bought.

This market stall in Clerkenwell has hardbacks and paperbacks available and a number of antiquarian books always for sale. The range is wide with non-fiction in the ascendancy and some specialisation in printing and architecture. The staff are friendly and helpful.

STOBART DAVIES LTD.
67-73 Worship Street, London EC2A 2EL.   071-247 0501

Subjects: Forestry, timber, woodworking.
Hours: Mon - Fri 9.30 - 5.30.
Services: Mail order, catalogues.

Stobart Davies Ltd. is a specialised mail order company situated between Liverpool Street and Moorgate on the fourth floor at 67-73 Worship Street. They claim to hold the finest stock of books on forestry, timber and woodworking anywhere in the world. In their showroom where customers are welcome to browse and/or buy, they have on display anything from one to two thousand titles relating to these subjects. Catalogues for mail order buyers are issued regularly.

BROWN & PERRING
36-44 Tabernacle Street, London EC2A 4DT.   071-253 4517

Subjects: Maritime books and charts.
Hours: Mon - Fri 9.00 - 5.15. Sat 9.00 - 12.00.
Services: Special orders, chart agents.

Expert advice is on hand for all who would go down to the sea. Brown and Perring are primarily chart agents and stockists of Admiralty publications. Commercial marine publications are available and a stock of yachting books has recently been added to their range.

JOHN MENZIES (G.B.) LTD.
56 Old Broad Street, London EC2M 1RX.   071-588 1632

Subjects: General, travel.
Hours: Mon - Fri 8.30 - 5.30.
Services: Credit cards.

A large lively shop with two sets of doors to the ground floor, where the general books and a well-stocked travel section are kept. A wide-ranging selection of paperbacks is stocked on the first floor. Author signing sessions are a strong feature. Many celebrated people from all walks of life and representing a wide variety of interests have attended these sessions to sign their own books.

BOOKS ETC.
30 Broadgate Circle, London EC2M 2QS. **071-628 8944**

Subjects: General.
Hours: Mon - Fri 8.00 - 8.00.
Services: Special orders, international mail order, credit cards.

This branch of Books Etc. in the Broadgate development is just one minute from Liverpool Street Station. The shop is particularly good on quality fiction, especially hardbacks. It has a comprehensive stock in all general sections, carefully selected business and computer books, a very popular cookery and wine section and a colourful display of cards and gift wrap for sale. A friendly shop with helpful staff, it is a pleasant place in which to browse.

OYEZ STATIONERY LTD.
105-107 Moorgate, London EC2M 6SL. **071-588 1478**

Subjects: Law.
Hours: Mon - Fri 8.45 - 5.15.
Services: Credit cards.

Primarily a stationers serving the City, the shop does stock a small but comprehensive range of law books.

A spacious premises with ledgers, legal tape and other appurtenances of the trade well displayed.

CITY POLY BOOKSHOP
Ground Floor, City of London Polytechnic,
84 Moorgate, London EC2M 6SQ. **071-638 2793**

Subjects: Study packs for: CIB, CIMA, ACCA, ICSA (professional bodies); accounting and finance, economics, law, marketing and management (new and secondhand student texts).
Hours: Mon - Fri 10.00 - 6.00.
Services: Account facilities, mail order, special orders, credit cards.

The most recent acquisition of the Economists' Bookshop group of specialist academic and professional booksellers, the City Poly branch boasts a wide range of new and secondhand recommended student texts. In addition, any book currently in print can be ordered on request.

W.H. SMITH LTD.
Western Mall, Liverpool Street Station,
London EC2M 7QA.   **071-628 1617**

Subjects: General.
Hours: Mon - Fri 7.00 - 8.00. Sat 8.00 - 5.00.
Services: Special orders, credit cards.

This branch of W.H. Smith is in the Mall leading from Liverpool
Street station to the Broadgate complex. It has a large paperback
fiction section, a standard range of general subjects and a small
children's section.

Bookstall opposite Platform 15.

Hours: Mon - Sat 6.30 a.m. - 7.45 p.m. Sun 8.00 - 7.45.

JOHN MENZIES (G.B.) LTD.
50 Cheapside, London EC2V 6AT.   **071-248 5315**

Subjects: General.
Hours: Mon - Fri 7.30 - 5.30.
Services: Credit cards.

This shop in the Menzies chain is one of the few to concentrate on
books and not have stationery. The range of stock is general but at
the popular end, with both hard and soft-backed books.

MUSEUM OF LONDON SHOP   **071-600 3699**
150 London Wall, London EC2Y 5HN.   **Ext 266**

Subjects: Books on London.
Hours: Tue - Sat 10.00 - 5.40. Sun 2.00 - 5.40.
Services: Mail order, catalogue.

The Museum of London is on the fringe of fortress-like Barbican.
The shop sells books on London, past and present, including novels,
plays and children's books; also archaeology, general and social
history with an urban application. A section on local history carries
many borough and local history society publications. Non-book
items are also available.

W.H. SMITH LTD.
145-147 Cheapside, London EC2Y 6BJ.   **071-606 2301**

Subjects: General.
Hours: Mon - Fri 8.30 - 5.30.
Services: Credit cards, special orders.

This branch has a general book department on the ground floor. There is a good British travel and camping guide section. The shop has the usual Smiths blend of magazines, books and stationery. There is a splendid view of St. Paul's Cathedral from the front of the shop.

BARBICAN MUSIC SHOP
Cromwell Tower, Whitecross Street,
Barbican, London EC2Y 8DD.   **071-588 9242**

Subjects: Music.
Hours: Mon - Fri 9.00 - 5.45. Sat 8.30 - 4.00.
Services: Mail order, catalogue, special orders, discounts, credit cards.

This bookshop is next door to the main entrance of the Barbican Centre, a few minutes' walk from the Barbican and Moorgate tube stations and equi-distant from each of them. It stocks books for the serious student (the Guildhall School of Music and Drama is nearby), school music books, biographies of composers, and has a large section on popular music, as well as musical accessories and a wide range of scores. A 10% discount is offered to professional musicians, teachers and students, and they operate a collection service from publishers, ensuring rapid delivery on special orders.

BARBICAN CENTRE SHOPS
The Barbican,   **071-638 4141**
London EC2Y 8DS.   **Ext. 322**

Subjects: Arts-related.
Hours: Level 4: Mon - Sat 11.00 - 9.30. Sun 12.00 - 9.00.
                 Level 7: Mon - Sat 10.30 - 7.30. Sun 12.00 - 7.30.
                 Level 8: Mon - Sat 10.00 - 6.45. Sun 12.00 - 5.45.
Services: Credit cards.

There are three bookshops in the Barbican. The shop on level 4 sells arts-related books. On level 7 there is a larger, more general bookshop which again reflects the arts activities of the centre, and on level 8 the Art Gallery Bookshop sells art books and exhibition-related merchandise.

ROYAL SHAKESPEARE COMPANY BOOKSTALL
Level 3, Stalls Left, Barbican Centre,
The Barbican, London EC2Y 8DS.   **071-628 3351**

Subjects: Shakespeare, drama.
Hours: 1 hour before performances till curtain up. Open during intervals.
Services: Credit cards.

This bookstall, run by the Royal Shakespeare Company, has a large selection of books on Shakespeare and his plays. Texts of current productions are available but they do not attempt to keep a large number of play texts. The Royal Shakespeare Company in Stratford-upon-Avon operate an extensive mail order service. (Tel. 0789-296655).

THE ECONOMISTS' BUSINESS BOOKSHOP   071-628 7479
9 Moorfields,   **24 hr. Answerphone 071-628 6453**
London EC2Y 9AE.   **Fax 071-482 4873**

Subjects: Banking, accountancy, business, law.
Hours: Mon - Fri 9.00 - 5.30.
Services: Credit cards, institutional supply, mail order, catalogue.

A well ordered shop nestling at the base of one of the City's towering office blocks, it serves the business and banking community around. The various subjects covered are clearly marked and the books arranged alphabetically within subject.

BOOKS ETC.
60 Fenchurch Street, London EC3M 4AQ.   **071-481 4425**

Subjects: General.
Hours: Mon - Fri 8.30 - 6.00.
Services: Special orders, international mailing, credit cards.

Once an old Post Office, this spacious branch of Books Etc. is conveniently placed for commuters using Fenchurch Street Station. There is a very wide range of hardback and paperback fiction and non-fiction. The travel department is particularly good with an excellent selection of maps, atlases, travel guides and glossy books. Business and computers, sport and other leisure interest titles are very well covered. This shop is a pleasant place to browse and the staff are helpful and friendly.

KELVIN HUGHES LTD.
(Incorporating J.D. Potter)
145 Minories, London EC3N 1NH.   **071-709 9076**

Subjects: Maritime books, Admiralty charts.
Hours: Mon - Fri 9.00 - 5.30.
Services: Mail order service (worldwide).

Established in 1830, this is a specialist bookshop catering for the yachtsman and for commercial shipping. Marine clothing and electronic instruments are stocked. The bookshop is two minutes away from Aldgate tube station.

NEW CITY BOOKSHOP
7 Byward Street, London EC3R 5AS.   **071-626 3649/3346**

Subjects: General, remainders.
Hours: Mon - Fri 9.00 - 5.30.
Services: Special orders.

On the ground floor the hardbacks are arranged by subject, with paperbacks downstairs. This amply stocked general bookshop has particularly good sections on business, religion and travel, and is an Open University stockist. There are tables of remainders on each floor.

TOWER BOOKSHOP
10 Tower Place, London EC3R 5BT.   **071-623 1081**

Subjects: General, tourist books.
Hours: Mon - Fri 9.30 - 6.00.
Services: Credit cards.

Books are shelved under subject headings but are selected for the needs of the tourists visiting the Tower of London so you can find the popular hardback under gardening and cookery with books on London also prominent. Souvenirs and cards take up a good deal of space so this is not the place for the serious bookworm.

SHERRATT & HUGHES
64-72 Leadenhall Market,   **071-626 5811**
London EC3V 1LT.   **City Department 071-623 9605**

Subjects: General, business.
Hours: Mon - Fri 8.30 - 5.30. Tue 9.30 - 5.30. Closed Sat and Bank Holidays.
Services: Special orders, credit accounts for institutional customers, free delivery within the City, mail order.

The Sherratt and Hughes Bookshop is situated in the centre of the Victorian Leadenhall Market, close to the heart of the City, with the stainless steel landmark of the Lloyd's building just outside. It is a large general bookshop with a particularly good range of maps and travel books, a small stationery department selling cards, pens and personalised stationery, and a specialist City Department with a comprehensive selection of books for the business community.

They are always happy to order titles that may not be in stock, and can draw on various specialised stock holdings at their other branches. They can offer credit accounts for institutional customers and free delivery within the City. Customers further afield may wish to have their books posted.

ASH RARE BOOKS
25 Royal Exchange, Threadneedle Street,
London EC3V 3LP. **071-626 2665**

Subjects: First editions, antiquarian books; antique maps and prints.
Hours: Mon - Fri 10.00 - 5.30.
Services: Mail order, catalogues, commissions, credit cards.

This small shop is built into the outer arches of the Royal Exchange. The rare and antiquarian books are in a small room at street level and a spiral staircase leads up to a gallery where antique maps and prints of London and all parts of the world are displayed. The window display of books is representative of the range with priced items such as a first edition of Dickens for £200.

EC4

Fetter Lane - Fleet Street - Ludgate Hill - St Paul's
- Cannon Street

OYEZ STATIONERY LTD.
144 Fetter Lane, London EC4A 1BT.   **071-405 2847**

Subjects: Legal books.
Hours: Mon - Fri 9.00 - 5.15.
Services: Special orders, credit cards.

Legal forms and general stationery are more prominent here than the
small book section but with the proximity of the Law Courts and
British libel laws, trade should be brisk.

JEWISH CHRONICLE BOOKSHOP
25 Furnival Street, London EC4A 1JT.   **071-405 9252**

Subjects: Judaism, books of Jewish interest.
Hours: Mon - Fri 9.30 - 5.00 (closed Fri afternoon).
Services: Lists, mail order, subscription to Jewish Chronicle.

This is the headquarters of the leading Jewish newspaper in the
country. In the reception area is a shop stocking books on Judaism
and of Jewish interest for adults and children. Book lists are
available on request.

HAMMICK'S LAW BOOKSHOP
Corner of Chancery Lane, 191/192 Fleet Street,   **071-405 5711**
London EC4A 2AH.   **Fax 071-831 9849**

Subjects: Law, business, computing, general.
Hours: Mon - Fri 9.00 - 6.00.
Services: Mail order, catalogue and specialist subject mailings,
journal subscriptions, credit cards.

Ideally situated in the heart of legal London and on the edge of the
City, offering probably the best range of law books in the country.
A spacious, fully air-conditioned shop on two floors. It provides a
comprehensive updating service for all legal and professional
publications. Special orders for books not in stock are always
welcome.

BOOKS ETC.
176 Fleet Street, London EC4A 2AB.   **071-353 5939**

Subjects: General.
Hours: Mon - Fri 8.30 - 6.30.
Services: Special orders, credit cards.

This branch of Books Etc. has recently moved to a spacious shop on two floors. There is a strong emphasis on new titles, in addition to a comprehensive stock of both hardback and paperback fiction and non-fiction. Travel, history, biography and business books are particularly well represented. A colourful range of cards and gift wrap is also on sale. The shop is well organised with friendly and helpful staff.

PROTESTANT TRUTH SOCIETY
184 Fleet Street, London EC4A 2HJ.   **071-405 4960**

Subjects: Christian literature (Evangelical and Protestant).
Hours: Mon - Fri 9.00 - 5.30.
Services: Mail order, special orders.

Well, both Protestantism and Fleet Street believe in the power of the word, so it should be a good address. Their principal stock is Bibles and Bible study literature, together with some popular Christian titles. As with most shops selling religious books there is an ample children's section and it also sells cards.

THE BOOKCASE
Roy Bloom Ltd.
26 Ludgate Hill, London EC4M 7DR.   **071-236 5982**

Subjects: General, remainders.
Hours: Mon - Fri 9.00 - 6.00 (Sun 12.00 - 4.00, Jun - Sep).
Services: Credit cards.

Another of those open, brightly lit places with generous displays of bargains. Besides remainders they stock full-price paperbacks, bestsellers and books of local and tourist interest.

READER'S DIGEST SHOP
9-10 Old Bailey, London EC4.   **071-409 5180**

Subjects: Readers Digest publications and other publishers, general.
Hours: Mon - Fri 8.30 - 5.00.
Services: Mail order, interest-free credit terms for Readers Digest products, credit cards.

The shop is next door to the Central Criminal Court, near St Paul's tube station. Its general sections include books on gardening, cookery, touring, travel, languages, DIY and reference; bestsellers only are stocked in paperback fiction. There are some street maps, guides and books of interest to tourists and overseas visitors. Good bargain books and reductions are always to be found at sale times. In addition, the shop sells a range of videos, greeting cards and Readers Digest music collections. The staff are helpful and friendly and the atmosphere is relaxed.

ACADEMIC BOOK EXCHANGE
20b Cathedral Place, London EC4M 7DY.   **071-236 7924**

Subjects: Academic.
Hours: Mon - Fri 11.00 - 4.00.
Services: Special orders.

A very small but worthwhile academic bookshop within the St Paul's Shopping Centre, stocking paperback titles, mainly in English but with a few in other European languages.

GEOGRAPHIA MAP SHOP
58 Ludgate Hill, London EC4M 7HX.   **071-248 3554**

Subjects: Maps, atlases, guides, globes.
Hours: Mon - Fri 9.00 - 5.15.
Services: Mail order, maps mounted, credit cards.

For the peregrinating journalist this store, with its well ordered displays, is a first resort. Coverage extends from town plans of Britain to globes of the world. Limitations of the site, prevent stocking titles in depth but their spectrum of coverage is broad and replenishment of stock frequent.

BOOKS NIPPON
Nippon Shuppan Hanbai UK Ltd.,
64-66 St Paul's Churchyard,
London EC4M 8AA.   **071-248 4956**

Subjects: Books in Japanese and books in English about Japan.
Hours: Mon - Fri 10.30 - 7.00. Sat 10.00 - 6.00.
Services: Special orders, credit cards.

A large modern shop selling Japanese music cassettes, gifts and fancy goods as well as books. They carry an extensive stock of Japanese publications, including maps and travel guides, and books in English relating to Japan and its culture.

ST PAUL'S CATHEDRAL BOOKSHOP
St Paul's Cathedral, London EC4M 8AD.   **no telephone**

Subjects: Christian literature.
Hours: Mon - Sat 11.00 - 4.15.

A small bookshop within the Cathedral stocking titles of Christian interest for adults and children and staffed by volunteer workers, the Friends of St Paul. There is also a separate shop which caters particularly for the tourist.

JONES & EVANS BOOKSHOP LTD.
70 Queen Victoria Street,
London EC4N 4SR.   **071-248 6516**

Subjects: General secondhand; London.
Hours: Mon - Fri 12.00 - 5.30.
Services: Special orders, library and institutional supplies.

A family business since 1816, the shop is the only general secondhand bookshop with a large stock in the City. Prices of books range from 50p upwards. There are both new and out-of-print books on London, its history, topography, flora, fauna and people.

W.H. SMITH LTD.
Station Bookshop, Cannon Street,
London EC4N 6AP.   **071-623 8230**

Subjects: Paperback fiction, bargain books.
Hours: Mon - Fri 7.00 - 6.30.

The shop in the railway station serves commuters to the City and is closed on Saturdays. There is a small paperback fiction section which includes bestsellers and two tables of bargain books. Newspapers, magazines and greetings cards are also stocked.

WITHERBY & CO. LTD.
147 Cannon Street, London EC4N 7BR.   **071-626 1912**

Subjects: Insurance, shipping, banking, management, dictionaries, travel and maps.
Hours: Mon - Fri 4.30 a.m. - 5.00 p.m.
Services: Mail order, special orders.

The long hours this shop keeps are because half of its business is as a newsagent and stationers. The books here are mainly on insurance and shipping, backed up a strong section of City of London type business books.

BANKERS BOOKS LTD.
17 St Swithins Lane, London EC4N 8AL.   **071-929 4306**

Subjects: Banking, finance, law, taxation, investment.
Hours: Mon - Fri 9.00 - 6.00.
Services: Special orders, library supply, global mail order, monthly new titles listing, credit cards.

Possibly the smallest (88 square feet) and certainly one of the most specialised bookshops in London, it stocks all the recommended reading for the examinations of the Chartered Institute of Bankers as well as a broad range of financial books from both U.K. and U.S.A. publishers. It is an International Chamber of Commerce agent and an importer of American Bankers Association titles.

SIMMONDS BOOKSHOP
16 Fleet Street, London EC4Y 1AX.   **071-353 3907**

Subjects: General, academic, journalism.
Hours: Mon - Fri 9.00 - 5.30.
Services: Mail order, library supply.

This narrow (10' wide) shop has been run by the Simmonds family since 1945. The premises are ancient and its history pre-dates Henry VIII. The general books are at ground floor level and the academic ones, which cover the nearby King's College syllabus, are in the basement. It is a busy shop and journalism features strongly on the shelves.

J. CLARKE-HALL LTD.
7 Bride Court (off Bride Lane),
Fleet Street, London EC4Y 8DU.   **071-353 4116**

Subjects: Antiquarian, secondhand, Johnsoniana, modern firsts, printing and book design, review copies.
Hours: Mon - Fri 10.30 - 6.30.
Services: Mail order, catalogues, library and institutional supply.

The shop is in a small arcade opposite St. Bride's Church and has a tiled front and windows protected by grills. There are many new-looking books for sale which are in fact review copies which carry a 20% price reduction. The shop specialises in work by and about Samuel Johnson, the great exemplar in these parts, who lived nearby. There is a good selection of antiquarian and secondhand books, and also some children's books. The same firm has a print shop at 22 Bride Lane, EC4, just across the road from the bookshop, whose stock includes nineteenth century topographical prints, mainly of the British Isles, and a good selection of Victorian greetings cards. A framing service is also available.

FAGINS BOOKSHOP
76 Upper Street, Islington, London N1 0NU.   **071-359 4699**

Subjects: General.
Hours: Mon - Sat 10.00 - 10.00.
Services: Special orders, postal service worldwide, school supply, credit cards.

This branch of Fagins offers a good range of fiction and new hardback titles and the non-fiction sections aim at diversity so that anyone from beginner to specialist might find something of interest. The computing section is unique to the area and the psychology section continues to grow in strength. There is a wide selection of cards and postcards. Customers are welcome to browse around this relaxed, well laid-out shop whose friendly staff are happy to help with enquiries.

G.W. WALFORD (BOOKSELLERS)
186 Upper Street. Islington, London N1 1RH.   **071-226 5682**

Subjects: Fine and rare antiquarian books.
Hours: Mon - Fri 9.30 - 4.30.
Services: Mail order catalogues.

A notice on the door makes it clear that browsers are not welcome but genuine collectors will be attended, although mail order is the main way business is conducted. Illustrated, travel and natural history are among the subjects, with sets of fine bindings and antiquarian books stocked. Rather sombre premises fronted by a window with an elegant piece of furniture and a book or two.

UPPER STREET BOOKSHOP
182 Upper Street, London, N1 1RQ.   **071-359 3785**

Subjects: General, art, architecture (secondhand).
Hours: Tue - Sat 9.30 - 6.00.
Services: Book search service, postal service.

Most of the books are priced between £5 and £50 but there is a selection of more valuable items. The stock is secondhand, both hard and paperbacked and all arranged in subject order. There is a section of books on architecture and Islington local history.

SISTER WRITE
190 Upper Street, London N1 1RQ.   **071-226 9782**

Subjects: Feminism, lesbianism, Black women's literature.
Hours: Mon - Sat 10.00 - 6.00. Thu 10.00 - 7.00.
Services: World wide mail order, credit cards.

This is a bookshop and craftshop run on co-operative lines by women and for women. In the bookshop there are books on women in history, politics, literature and on many other aspects of women's lives. The craftshop side of the business sells jewellery, pottery, candles and T-shirts. The whole shop is accessible to wheelchairs.

T. MILES & CO. LTD.
276 St Paul's Road, Islington,
London N1 2LH.   **071-226 3445**

Subjects: General, fishing, maps and guides, languages.
Hours: Mon - Fri 9.00 - 5.30. Sat 9.30 - 4.00.
Services: Special orders.

The shop has a good general range but is strong on fishing, maps and guides. They are school and library suppliers.

CANONBURY BOOKSHOP
Islington Books Ltd.
268 Upper Street, London N1 2UQ.   **071-226 3475**

Subjects: General, children's, art, travel, maps, local history.
Hours: Mon - Sat 9.00 - 6.00.
Services: Special orders, postal service, credit cards.

An unusual shop with a unique atmosphere and a reputation for speed of service and the ability to supply that elusive title. In the basement is their special children's department which many of their customers have likened to an Aladdin's cave. Apart from carrying a fine selection of reading material, they stock a wide range of educational and traditional wooden toys as well as jigsaws, games and other interesting book-orientated toys.

On the ground floor is a range of general books which is surprisingly varied for the size of the shop. They also stock stationery, both for personal and business requirements, quality greetings cards including designs of local interest, and a select range of gifts from all over the world.

SCM BOOKROOM
26-30 Tottenham Road, London N1 4BZ.   **071-249 7262/5**

Subjects: Religion, theology.
Hours: Mon - Fri 9.00 - 5.00.
Services: Special orders, mail order, catalogue, credit cards.

Within the premises of SCM Press in Dalston, the Bookroom carries a carefully chosen stock from all major British and American publishers, covering all aspects of the Christian religion and theology, with a further section on World religions. Visitors are welcome, though the business is mainly mail order and they produce an excellent catalogue. Most of the books are in pristine condition but twice yearly a sale is held of damaged stock, mainly SCM titles.

CND BOOKSHOP
22-24 Underwood Street, London N1 7JQ.   **071-250 4010**

Subjects: The nuclear debate, green issues.
Hours: Tue - Thu 10.00 - 4.00.
Services: Mail order, catalogue.

The bookshop is in one large room on the ground floor where it displays a large stock of books and pamphlets on the nuclear debate and green issues.

STRIKE ONE (ISLINGTON) LTD.
51 Camden Passage, Islington,
London N1 8EA.   **071-226 9709**

Subjects: Horology, new, secondhand and antiquarian.
Hours: Mon - Sat 9.00 - 5.00.
Services: Special orders, search service, credit cards.

This company is a supplier of antique clocks and barometers. There is a bookshop on the premises stocking books relating to their specialist field.

ANGEL BOOKSHOP
102 Islington High Street, London N1 8EG.   **071-226 2904**

Subjects: General, reference books on antiques.
Hours: Mon - Sat 9.30 - 6.00.
Services: Special orders, postal service.

The speciality of this bookshop is a good antique reference section which must be welcomed by the many antique dealers in the area. General subjects are well stocked as is hardback fiction, and there is an excellent paperback department at the rear of the shop. They have a strong children's section and cooking and wine are well represented.

W.H. SMITH LTD.
King's Cross Station, London N1 9AP.   **071-837 5580**

Subjects: General.
Hours: Mon - Sat 7.00 - 8.45. Sun 8.00 - 7.45.
Services: Credit cards. Special orders.

Quite a large shop at King's Cross with access from the street or the station. General subjects are covered in hardback and paperback with people working in the vicinity in mind as well as travellers.

HOUSMANS BOOKSHOP LTD.
5 Caledonian Road,
King's Cross, London N1 9DX.   **071-837 4473**

Subjects: Pacifism, anarchism, gay and feminist literature.
Hours: Mon - Fri 10.00 - 6.00. Sat 10.00 - 1.00. 1.30 - 5.00
Services: Special orders, mail order catalogue, distribution service to the book trade.

This bookshop near King's Cross Station has a wide range of books orientated to its own specialist subjects. The pacifist, anarchist and anti-military department and a large range of left wing magazines and journals are at the rear of the shop. The rest of the ground floor is more general in subject but very much in line with the left movement. Plenty of room upstairs and downstairs in which to browse.

VICTORS (MODEL RAILWAYS)
166 Pentonville Road, London N1 9JL.　　　　**071-278 1019**

Subjects:　Overseas and model railways.
Hours:　　Mon - Sat 10.00 - 5.30.
Services:　Mail order, special orders.

A small shop concentrating on model railways supported by a book section on overseas railways (mainly European and American) by foreign publishers. There are about twenty-five monthly magazines from abroad on overseas railways and overseas model railways. An interesting shop for the railway buff.

STAINER & BELL LTD.
123 High Road, East Finchley, London N2 8AG.   **081-444 9135**

Subjects: Music, worship, hymnody.
Hours: Mon - Fri 9.00 - 5.00.
Services: Mail order, catalogue.

This is the distribution office of Stainer & Bell, the music publishers, but is open to the public — who will probably need to refer to the publishers' catalogue, as only a few books are on display.

MARTIN THE NEWSAGENT
29-31 Ballards Lane, Finchley, London N3 1XP.   **081-346 9303**

Subjects: General, children's.
Hours: Mon - Wed & Sat 8.30 - 6.00. Thu 8.30 - 7.00. Fri 8.30 - 7.00.
Services: Credit cards, special orders.

A stationers and booksellers with the usual range of general stock. Some headings are Hobbies — T.V. — Adventure — Horror. Maps and guides are sold.

FACULTY BOOKS
98 Ballards Lane, London N3 2DN.   **081-346 7761/0145**

Subjects: General, academic, children's.
Hours: Mon - Sat 9.30 - 5.30.
Services: Special orders, school and library supply.

An excellent general bookshop. There is another branch of the shop at the Middlesex Polytechnic, which stocks books on law and business studies.

MANOR HOUSE BOOKS
80 East End Road, London N3 2SY.   **081-349 9484**

Subjects: Judaica, Middle East, theology.
Hours: Mon - Thu 10.00 - 4.00. Fri 10.00 - 1.00. Sun 10.00 - 2.00. Other times by appointment.
Services: Special orders, search service, mail order, catalogue.

Within the precincts of The Sternberg Centre for Judaism in Finchley, this small shop carries an exceedingly well-chosen stock on Judaism, Jewish history and culture, and Old Testament studies. The books, new and secondhand, are mainly in English, with some in Hebrew and a few in Yiddish. There is a large children's section. The owner's interests extend further afield — he runs Middle East Books as a mail order business (secondhand and antiquarian) from his home in Whetstone: 01-445 4293.

THE MUSLIM INFORMATION SERVICE
233 Seven Sisters Road, London N4 2DA.   **071-272 5170**

Subjects: Islam, books in English and Arabic.
Hours: Mon - Fri 9.30 - 5.30. Sat 10.00 - 6.00.
Services: Mail order, catalogue, lists, lectures, cassettes.

Books on Islam, scholarly and devotional, well displayed in one spacious room. There are special sections for children and for schools.

BOOKMARKS
265 Seven Sisters Road, Finsbury Park,
London N4 2DE.   **081-802 6145/8873**

Subjects: Leftwing literature, international politics, social sciences, health, psychology, environment, fiction, poetry, children's, periodicals, secondhand and remainders.
Hours: Mon - Sat 10.00 - 6.00. Wed 10.00 - 7.00.
Services: Mail order service for socialists and trade unionists, specialist socialist book club, credit cards (also by telephone).

Bookmarks is a specialist bookshop on two floors whose varied stock shows obvious strengths in the area of left wing political theory, trade unionism and the politics of oppressed and minority groups. Cultural and social studies are also a strength: there is a large fiction section, a good selection of books on the other arts and a well-stocked social sciences section. At the very back of the shop is a room largely devoted to a wide selection of children's picture and story books, the latter arranged by age group. Also in this room is a good selection of books on international politics arranged by geographical area. Upstairs is the secondhand and remainders section, as well as books on trade unionism, Marxism and Bookmarks' own publications.

Bookmarks has a quarterly book club and a comprehensive mail order service. It is affiliated to the Socialist Workers Party and includes their publications and agit-prop section.

NEW BEACON BOOKSHOP
76 Stroud Green Road, London N4 3EN.   **071-272 4889**

Subjects: Caribbean, African, Afro-American, Black British.
Hours: Tue - Sat 10.30 - 6.00 (Mon closed).
Services: Catalogue, mail order, library supply, special orders, credit cards.

Black fiction, poetry and criticism as well as politics, history, sociology and economics. A good selection of books for children of African and Caribbean descent. Music and cook books relating to these countries are also sold.

NEW ERA BOOKS AND HANDICRAFTS
203 Seven Sisters Road, London N4 3NG.   **071-272 5894**

Subjects: Marxist-Leninist, Chinese, anti-imperialist.
Hours: Tue - Fri 10.00 - 5.30. Sat 11.00 - 4.00.
Services: Mail order, catalogue.

The Marxist classics and Mao, who is still in their pantheon, predominate, but there are strong sections too on Third World subjects and national liberation movements. This company is also a wholesale distributor of books from China. Sinophiles, post 1949, will find plenty to interest them here.

SUNPOWER, WHOLEFOOD,
CRAFT & BOOK CO-OPERATIVE
198 Blackstock Road, Highbury, London N5   **071-704 0247**

Subjects: Green issues, food/cookery, alternative medicine, personal development, spirituality, fiction, anarchism, children's.
Hours: Mon 10.00 - 8.00. Tue - Sat 10.00 - 6.00.

This shop is run as a workers' co-operative and sells wholefoods and non-exploitative crafts from Third World co-operatives and local craftspeople as well as books. The book stock offers a range of 'alternatives' - such as vegetarian and vegan food and cookery and alternative medicine, including herbalism. There are books on spirituality and personal development, astrology and tarot. Women's and Black fiction, non-sexist, non-racist children's books, books on anarchism and radical/political magazines are also stocked.

H.H. SALES LTD. (formerly Harry Hayes)
Clarendon Buildings, 25 Horsell Road,
Highbury, London N5 1XJ.   **071-607 5505**

Subjects: Philately, postal history, postcards and related background history and topography.
Hours: Mon - Fri 10.15 - 7.30 (variable).
Services: Postal auctions, wants lists, credit cards.

This is not a conventional bookshop but a showroom housing around ten thousand books on philately and postal history, probably the largest stock in the world on these subjects. They hold four postal sales a year and believe they are the only firm in the world solely dedicated to such auctions in this field. It is advisable to telephone before calling as a casual visitor might be disappointed. The nearest underground is at Holloway Road.

THE CHOLMELEY BOOKSHOP
W.E. Hersant Ltd.,
228 Archway Road, London N6 5AZ.   **081-340 3869**

Subjects: Military, Aviation.
Hours: Mon - Sat 9.30 - 1.00. 2.00 - 5.30. (closed Thu).
Services: Special orders, mail order, credit cards.

This shop is a 5 minute downhill walk from Highgate tube station.
The books are well ordered with each specialist subject divided into
new and secondhand stock. They have a large range of U.K. and
overseas titles on aviation, naval and military matters. Some general
titles are also stocked.

BONAVENTURE
259 Archway Road, London N6 5BS.   **081-341 2345**

Subjects: General, travel (secondhand)
Hours: Wed - Sat 11.00 - 6.00. Mon, Tue closed.
Services: Search service, books bought.

This small shop specializes in secondhand travel books, covering
many areas, particularly Latin America but it also has a range of
general secondhand books and a worthwhile foreign language
section. On Mondays and Tuesdays the shop is closed because the
owner is out hunting down choice items for his stock.

FISHER AND SPERR
46 Highgate High Street, London N6 5JB.   **081-340 7244**

Subjects: General (antiquarian and secondhand)
Hours: Mon - Sat 10.00 - 5.30.
Services: Credit cards, 'Wants' list welcome.

This is an attractive seventeenth century, timber framed, bow-
windowed, four storied cornucopia of secondhand and antiquarian
books. There are 50,000 various titles which Mr. Sperr has lovingly
assembled, as collecting is his hobby. The subject range is universal,
but books about London have a special place in this splendid shop.

HIGHGATE BOOKSHOP
9 Highgate High Street, London N6 5JR.   **081-340 5625**

Subjects: General.
Hours: Tue - Sat 9.30 - 5.30.
Services: Special orders, credit cards.

This attractive, white clapboard-faced shop holds a prominent corner position in Highgate for its excellent general stock of paperbacks and hardbacks. No technical books available but the most popular sections, namely children's and cookery, are well stocked and easily accessible.

HOLLOWAY STATIONERS AND BOOKSELLERS
357 Holloway Road, London N7 0RN.   **071-607 3972**

Subjects: General.
Hours: Mon - Sat 9.00 - 6.00.
Services: Special orders, credit cards.

A stationers, but with a generous proportion given over to popular paperbacks, fiction and non-fiction, including revision aids. There are also reference, travel, leisure interest and children's books.

JONES BROTHERS
340-366 Holloway Road, London N7 6NY.   **071-607 2727**

Subjects: General, children's.
Hours: Tue, Thu, Fri 9.00 - 5.30. Wed 9.30 - 7.30. Sat 9.00 - 6.00. Closed Mon.

The long-established children's book department is adjacent to toys. The newer general book department (which opened on the first floor in 1987) carries a wide selection. There is a buttery on the first floor. The store is a branch of the John Lewis Partnership.

FANTASY CENTRE
157 Holloway Road, London N7 8LX.   **071-607 9433**

Subjects: Sci-Fi, Horror, Fantasy (secondhand).
Hours: Mon - Fri 10.00 - 6.00. Sat 10.00 - 5.00.
Services: Mail order, catalogue, wants list.

The shop covers its speciality well, selling secondhand hardbacks and paperbacks, magazines and ephemera. At the rear is a section of first editions and collectors' items including some 19th century detective fiction.

CROUCH END BOOKSHOP
60 Crouch End Hill, London N8 8AG.   **081-348 8966**

Subjects: General, new, secondhand and antiquarian.
Hours: Mon - Sat 9.00 - 6.00.
Services: Special orders, credit cards.

Located in an attractive corner situation, it has a good general range
of hard and soft covered books, both new and secondhand.

BARGAIN BOOKSHOP
2 Concourse, Edmonton Green, London N9 OTY. **081-807 7972**

Subjects: General.
Hours: Mon 9.30 - 4.00. Tue - Sat 9.30 - 5.30.
Services: Special orders, credit cards.

The shop is at the bus stop entrance to the shopping centre. The
stock is a mix of hardback and paperback books plus a few
remainders.

MUSWELL HILL BOOKSHOP
Fagins Bookshops (Muswell Hill) Ltd.
72 Fortis Green Road, Muswell Hill,
London N10 3HN.   **081-444 7588**

Subjects: General, travel.
Hours: Mon - Fri 9.30 - 6.00. Sat 9.30 - 5.30.
Services: Special orders, postal service, credit cards.

An excellent general bookshop which omits only childrens books,
there being that sort of shop opposite. All is well ordered and the
place gives an impression of abundance. The fiction section is
generous and they stock Open University course books. Special
orders are welcome.

W.H. SMITH LTD.
117 Muswell Hill Broadway,
Muswell Hill, London N10 3RS.   **081-883 1706**

Subjects: General.
Hours: Mon - Sat 8.30 - 5.30.
Services: Credit cards, special orders.

Quite a small Smith's selling general titles. Books occupy about 25% of the space with stationery, news, and toys taking up the rest.

CHILDREN'S BOOKSHOP (MUSWELL HILL)
29 Fortis Green Road, London N10 3RT.   **081-444 5500**

Subjects: Children's books.
Hours: Mon - Fri 9.15 - 5.45. Sat 9.15 - 5.30.
Services: Special orders, credit card, 'Post a Book'.

A bright and cheerful shop with discreet expertise on hand. Books to appeal to children from the beginning up to twelve or thirteen. There are no severe gradings of the stock by age group, which can of course embarrass any of us under a hundred.

DENIS CAINE BOOKS.
343 Bowes Road, London N11 1AA.   **081-361 4888**

Subjects: General (secondhand and antiquarian), maps and prints.
Hours: Mon - Sat 10.00 - 5.00.

An interesting secondhand and antiquarian shop with a bias towards literature and modern first editions, run by the owner. The sort of shop the metropolitan bibliophile likes to browse in.

HELGATO BOOKS
2 The Broadway,
Friern Barnet Road, London N11 3DU.   **081-361 8326**

Subjects: Topography,   natural   history,   illustrated   books
            (antiquarian).
Hours: Wed - Sat 9.30 - 5.30.
Services: Mail order.

The specialities of this business are topography, natural history and illustrated books, together with antiquarian maps and prints.

CORNERSTONE
The Finchley Christian Bookshop, 638 High Road,
North Finchley, London N12 ONL   **081-446 3056**

Subjects: Christian literature.
Hours: Mon - Sat 9.30 - 5.30. Fri 9.30 - 6.30
Services: Special orders, school and church supply.

An Evangelical Christian bookshop with the accustomed mix of Bibles, Bible study aids, popular and children's books. An attractive and friendly shop.

HATCHARDS
782 High Road, North Finchley, London N12 8JY. 081-446 9669

Subjects: General.
Hours: Mon - Fri 9.00 - 5.30.
Services: Special orders, school suppliers, out-of-print book search, credit cards.

This most recently opened bookshop in the Hatchards group is on the busy main road of Finchley only five minutes away from Woodside Park tube station. In addition to a comprehensive range of both general and academic titles, the shop also carries an attractive selection of cards and gift wrap. It is a pleasant place in which to browse. There is also a special children's corner.

W.H. SMITH LTD.
766 High Road, North Finchley, London N12 9QH. 081-445 2785

Subjects: General.
Hours: Mon - Sat 9.00 - 6.00. Thu 9.30 - 5.30.
Services: Special orders, credit cards.

No nasty surprises for fans of smaller W.H.S's here, everything as it should be, with children's books getting a special mention.

W.H. SMITH LTD.
5 Alderman's Hill, Palmers Green, London N13 4YD. 081-886 4743

Subjects: General.
Hours: Mon - Sat 8.30 - 5.30.
Services: Credit cards, special orders.

Because of a dearth of bookshops in the area at least one third of the space here is for bookselling. The books themselves are general and of popular interest.

AUTOLYCUS
63 Chase Side, Southgate, London N14 5BU.   **081-886 9889**

Subjects: General, bargain books.
Hours: Mon - Fri 9.30 - 5.30. Sat 9.00 - 6.00.
Services: Library supply, credit cards.

Named after Shakespeare's "snapper-up of unconsidered trifles", this new bookshop, two minutes from Southgate tube station aims to provide as wide a range as possible of remainders, premiums and publishers' overstocks. Some browsers spend so much time here that they have even provided chairs!

OAKHILL COLLEGE BOOKROOM
Oak Hill College, Chase Side,
Southgate, London N14 4PS.   **081-449 3162**

Subjects: Theology.
Hours: Mon 9.00 - 12.00, 2.00 - 5.00. Tue 2.00 - 6.00, 7.00 - 7.30. Thu 3.00 - 5.00. Fri 2.00 - 5.00.
Services: Special orders.

The shop is just inside the entrance to this Anglican theological college. They stock, with their students very much in mind, commentaries, Bibles, hymn books and a small general range of soft backed Christian literature.

SOUTHGATE BOOK SHOP
62 Chase Side, London N14 5PA.   **081-882 5690**

Subjects: General.
Hours: Mon - Fri 9.30 - 6.00. Sat 9.00 - 6.00.
Services: Special orders, school and library supplier.

A recently fitted-out, modern bookshop carrying a wide range of paperbacks in all subjects and including a strong literary content. There is a range of fiction and non-fiction in hardback, a good travel guide section and an important children's corner. General educational, professional, reference and computer books are also stocked. There is a special order service for customers.

ARMS AND MILITARIA BOOKSHOP
34 High Street, Southgate, London N14 6EE.　　　**081-886 0334**

Subjects:　Weapons and militaria, mainly secondhand.
Hours:　Mon, Wed & Sat 9.30 - 5.00. Fri 9.30 - 4.00. Closed Tue & Thu.
Services:　Institute and library supply.

A good specialist shop whose title explains itself. Within its field they have regimental histories, the development of weaponry and books on military uniforms. The staff is expert and the shop covers the field from the sixteenth century to the present.

WORM BOOKS
36 Conway Road, London N14 7BE.　　　**081-886 5799**

Services:　Bookfinding.

No shop, no stock. Bookfinding service only. Telephone or postal contact is preferred but visitors are welcome.

Worm Books has been included here because, although not a bookshop, it provides a very useful service not always available at a bookshop: a bookfinding service. This is the owner's preferred term as being more positive than 'booksearch' or 'search service'.

HEADSTART BOOKS & CRAFTS
25 West Green Road, London N15 5BX   **081-802 2838**

Subjects: Black interest.
Hours: Mon - Thu 9.30 - 6.30. Fri - Sat 9.30 - 7.00.
Services: Special orders, school and library supply.

As its name indicates, this is in part a craft shop, but so far as the books are concerned they are exclusively by or for or about Black people worldwide.

ETERNAL COMICS
695 Seven Sisters Road,
Tottenham, London N15 5LA.   **081-809 2022**

Subjects: Comics (Marvel/DC/Independent), graphic novels, comic-related news magazines, posters, original art-work.
Hours: Mon 11.00 - 7.00. Tue - Thu 11.00 - 6.00. Fri 11.00 - 7.00. Sat 10.00 - 7.00.
Services: Search service, mail order, subscription service, credit cards.

Small but perfectly formed specialists *(sic)* in imported American comics, the shop is ideally located only feet from Seven Sisters tube station. Back issues are available and fresh stock comes in every Thursday and Friday afternoon. The staff are courteous and friendly and have a broad knowledge of the stock.

VORTEX GALLERIES
139-141 Stoke Newington Church Street,
London N16 OHU.   **071-254 6516**

Subjects: General, art, humanities (secondhand and antiquarian).
Hours: Mon - Sat 11.00 - 6.00. Sun 1.00 - 6.00.
Services: Books bought, credit cards.

A large browsing space for the many books on general subjects held by Vortex in a rather sparse setting but supported by a shop selling artists' materials and a café which is open until 11 pm every night for jazz concerts.

CIRCA
144 Stoke Newington Church Street,
London N16 0JU.   **071-249 9775**

Subjects: General secondhand.
Hours: Mon - Fri 12.30 - 6.00. Sat 11.30 - 6.00.
Services: Books bought.

Modern literature and academic paperbacks are prominent among the books. The shop also sells new and 'period' china, jewellery and greetings cards.

STOKE NEWINGTON BOOKSHOP
153 Stoke Newington High Street,
London N16 0NY.   **071-249 2808**

Subjects: General, children's.
Hours: Mon - Sat 9.30 - 5.30.
Services: Special orders, school supply, credit cards.

This well-stocked general bookshop is bright and attractively designed. There is a comprehensive selection of paperback and hardback fiction whilst non-fiction ranges from travel and the arts through to green politics. The children's section is particularly strong. Older children appreciate the wide selection and toddlers enjoy playing with the toys and 'reading copies'. All areas reflect the wide cross-section of the local communities. The lively and helpful staff are always ready to assist should you be unable to find what you want.

A. BRAUN (HEBREW BOOKSELLERS)
82 Dunsmure Road,   **081-800 5863**
London N16 5JY.   **Fax 081-809 5008**

Subjects: Rabbinical literature in Hebrew and English.
Hours: Mon - Thu 10.00 - 7.00. Fri, Sun 10.00 - 2.00. (Variable)
Services: Old Hebrew books bought.

This bookshop serves a wide local Jewish community. It stocks Rabbinical literature mainly in Hebrew but there are also some English translations. Jewish requisites may be bought here.

THE HEBREW BOOK
AND GIFT CENTRE
18 Cazenove Road, London N16 6BD

Daytime 071-254 3963
Evening 081-802 4567

Subjects: Rabbinical literature in Hebrew and English.
Hours: Mon - Thu 10.00 - 5.00. Fri & Sun 10.00 - 2.00.
Services: Mail order, credit cards.

As well as the religious books there is quite a range of general. There is a huge selection of Talmud and Code of Law books, a special collection of Cantorial and Chassidic cassette tapes and a wide range of Hebrew and English fiction. Hebrew is spoken in the shop, which also sells other items pertinent to the faith.

UNIVERSAL BOOKSHOP LTD.
Metaphysical and Inspirational World,
4 Cazenove Road, Stamford Hill,
London N16 6BD.

071-241 5509

Subjects: Metaphysical, mystical, health, contemporary religion.
Hours: Mon - Fri 10.30 - 7.00. Sat 10.00 - 4.00.
Services: Mail order, special orders within their subject field.

Probably the only bookshop in North London specialising in metaphysical, mystical and inspirational books - in mind, body and spirit. It could be the place for those on a spiritual quest or hoping to achieve spiritual growth. Other items on offer include mystical oils, tapes, incense, candles and crystals.

MESOIROH SEFORIM BOOKSTORE LTD.
61 Oldhill Street,
London N16 6LU.

081-809 4310
Fax 081-802 1390

Subjects: Judaica in Hebrew and English.
Hours: Mon - Thu 8.30 - 6.45. Fri, Sun 8.30 - 1.00.

The books here are in both Hebrew and English, including some children's and educational books. Religious requisites are also sold. They provide such useful services as photocopying and laminating. Another side of their business is the publishing of Hebrew books.

STOKE NEWINGTON & NORTH HACKNEY
LABOUR PARTY BOOKSHOP
Service East Ltd., 96a Stoke Newington High Street,
London N16 7NY.   071-249 5624

Subjects: General, politics, economics (mainly secondhand).
Hours: Mon 11.00 - 4.30. Tue - Sat 10.30 - 4.30.
Services: Books bought.

A good stock of paperback and hardback fiction and non-fiction
in addition to the shop's speciality which is politics. As well as
secondhand books this section includes some new ones on the labour
movement. As about a third of the books are donated, prices are
low.

STAMFORD HILL BOOKSHOP
Church House, Portland Avenue,
London N16 7TH.   081-809 4922/4995

Subjects: General, secondhand and antiquarian.
Hours: Mon - Fri 9.30 - 5.00. Sat 10.30 - 4.30. Wed closed.
Services: Library supply, mail order catalogues.

Housed in the former choir vestry of the church, this shop defies
logic by fitting some twelve thousand titles into a room designed for
half that amount, whilst still managing to look spacious enough for
browsers. This could have something to do with the twelve foot high
bookcases and the well-ordered stock. Described at intervals by
customers as an oasis, Tardis or, less flatteringly, as a rabbit warren,
the stock is comprehensive. Links with reviewers of leading literary
journals ensure a constant flow of quality academic review copies at
half price.

PENDLEBURYS
Church House, Portland Avenue,
London N16 7TH.   081-809 4922/4995

Subjects: Theology, secondhand and antiquarian.
Hours: Mon - Fri 9.30 - 5.00. Sat 10.30 - 4.30. Wed closed.
Services: Library suppliers, mail order catalogues.

Sharing premises with the Stamford Hill bookshop, this business is devoted entirely to the supply of academic theology. Some six thousand secondhand volumes, dating from the sixteenth century onwards, are on view with a back-up stock of another five hundred. The shop is supplier to more than a hundred libraries in twenty-three countries.

R.H. FAULKS & CO.
2 St Loys Road, London N17 6UA.   **081-808 3646**

Subjects: General, educational
Hours: Mon - Sat 10.00 - 5.30
Services: Special orders.

Stationery is the seller here but in a side room is a small quantity of general books on 'A', 'O' and C.S.E. exams and some on computers.

COMYNS BOOKS
61 Sterling Way, London N18 2UE.   **081-807 3427**

Subjects: General paperbacks, maps.
Hours: Mon - Wed 9.30 - 6.00. Fri 9.30 - 6.00. Sat 9.00 - 6.00.
Services: Credit cards, a book exchange service (half back credit).

This has been a bookshop for a hundred years though the 'girlie' magazines were probably under the counter then. All the books are paperbacks and they can be exchanged as well as purchased.

G.W. FOOTE & CO.
702 Holloway Road, London N19 3NL.   **071-272 1266**

Subjects: Humanism, rationalism, secularism, free thought.
Hours: Mon - Fri 9.15 - 5.30.
Services: Mail order, list.

The publishers of 'The Freethinker' share an office with the
National Secular Society in this down-at-heel stretch of Holloway
Road (reached from Archway tube). They carry an interesting stock
of books on their specialism, from various publishers, and some
even more interesting pamphlets — on such subjects as 'The
Unpleasant Personality of Jesus Christ'.

THE AVIATION BOOKSHOP
656 Holloway Road, London N19 3PD   **071-272 3630**

Subjects: Aviation, new and secondhand.
Hours: Mon - Sat 9.30 - 5.30.
Services: Credit cards, international mail order, special orders,
catalogue.

'A unique shop in Europe' was how a passing German customer
described this place. This is no catchpenny title, but exactly
describes the shop's universal coverage of man and flight. The
books are new and secondhand and the shop is bedecked with
model aircraft and interesting bits of real aircraft which make it a
fascinating place to browse around. The staff are, of course, expert,
and besides the books on sale there are also related magazines and
pin-up photos of your favourite aircraft.

GREEN INK BOOKSHOP
8 Archway Mall, Junction Road,
London N19 5RG.   **071-263 4748**

Subjects: Books from and about Ireland and the Irish.
Hours: Mon - Sat 10.00 - 6.00.
Services: Library services, community bookstalls, credit cards.

They claim to be the largest exclusively Irish bookshop in Europe. There are sections on fiction, history, politics, literature, sport, food, photography, travel etc.; children's books and maps, a stock of books in the Irish language, and a music section with books and cassettes. The shop is conveniently located just twenty yards from the rear of Archway tube station.

WHETSTONE BOOKS
368 Oakleigh Road North, London N20 0SP.   **071-368 8338**

Subjects: General (secondhand).
Hours: Tue, Wed, Fri 9.30 - 3.00. Sat 10.00 - 5.00.
Services: Books bought, search service.

One room filled with books on many things, all secondhand. The diligent searcher after an overlooked first imprint might have his or her senses alerted here. The Penguin shelves are particularly well stocked.

MORGANS & CO. LTD.
1287 High Road, London N20 9HS.   **081-445 2692**

Subjects: General.
Hours: Mon - Sat 9.00 - 5.00. Thu 9.00 - 1.00.

This is an emporium with books included; study aids are well represented.

CHATTERBOOX
136 Myddleton Street, Wood Green,
London N22 4NQ.   **081 889 9875**

Subjects: Christian literature, general.
Hours: Mon - Sat 9.00 - 5.00. Thu 9.00 - 1.30.
Services: Mail order, church bookstalls, schools supplier, credit cards.

This bookshop stocks a range of Christian books, the majority of them on eschatological subjects, and Christian-related fiction. There are videos for hire and a café where customers may relax and chat.

BOOTS THE CHEMISTS
137-139 High Road, Wood Green Shopping City,
London N22 6BA.   **081-888 0101**

Subjects: General.
Hours: Mon - Wed 9.00 - 5.30. Thu 9.00 - 7.30. Fri & Sat 9.00 - 6.00.
Services: Credit cards.

The books are found on the first floor of this branch of Boots. They are general, popular and hard and soft backed. Alas this chain of shops was once renowned more for books than soap.

READING MATTERS BOOKSHOP
Reading Matters Ltd., 187 High Road,
Wood Green, London N22 6BA.   **081-881 3187**

Subjects: Community politics, women's issues, Black studies, ecology, green politics, New Age, children's.
Hours: Mon - Sat 9.30 - 6.00.
Services: Special orders, school and library supply, bookstall service for schools and community groups, photocopying.

Reading Matters, located in the Library Mall, is Haringey's community bookshop. Its speciality is non-sexist, non-racist books for adults and children, with the children's books in community languages as well as in English. Generally the stock offers radical alternatives across the spectrum from health to politics.

W.H. SMITH LTD.
110 High Road,
Wood Green Shopping City, London N22 6HE.   **081-889 0221**

Subjects: General, educational, children's.
Hours: Mon - Sat 9.00 - 6.00. Thu 9.00 - 8.00.
Services: Credit cards, special orders.

One of the best W.H. Smith's for books in North London, with the whole of the first floor selling them. The department is spacious and well laid out with a good bargain book selection and separate sections for educational books and children's books. It is due to undergo extensive modernisation starting in January 1990.

NURSING BOOK SERVICE LTD.
52 Phoenix Road, Euston,
London NW1 1ES.   **071-387 9378**

Subjects: Nursing, medical.
Hours: Mon - Fri 8.00 - 5.00.
Services: University and library supply, mail order.

This shop specialises in nursing and medical books. The staff pride
themselves on their mail order service.

FRIENDS BOOK CENTRE
Friends House, Euston Road,
London NW1 2BJ.   **071-387 3601 Ext. 23**

Subjects: Quakerism and allied subjects.
Hours: Mon - Fri 9.30 - 5.30, Sat occasionally.
Services: Mail order, catalogue, special orders, discount for
                bookshops.

Opposite Euston Station is a large stone building named Friends
House and on the ground floor is the Quaker Book Centre. It is the
only bookshop in the British Isles to specialise and stock such a large
number of British and American Quaker publications. It is their aim
to be an outlet for religious literature and fringe subjects, so as well
as their very comprehensive Quaker section they stock books on
ecology, biography, conservation, vegetarianism and other relevant
subjects. Children's books and study packs also have their place
with sections on classes for parents and teachers. The shop also
specialises in secondhand and remainder books on Quakerism, and
a selection of secondhand religious and general books is also
available.

JOHN MENZIES (G.B.) LTD.
Main Bookstall, Euston Station,
London NW1 2DU.   **071-387 4640**

Subjects: General.
Hours: Mon - Sun 6.00 - 10.00
Services: Credit cards.

The main bookstall is to the left of the entrance to Euston station.
Paperback fiction is arranged by publisher and there are some
fiction titles in hardback. Travel, transport (mainly railways),
business and reference are among the non-fiction subjects stocked,
and a table displays bargain books in hardback. Also available are
newspapers, magazines, confectionery and tobacco.

JOHN MENZIES (G.B.) LTD.
The Colonade, Euston Station,
London NW1 2DU.   **071-387 5354**

Subjects: General.
Hours: Mon - Sat 7.00 - 10.00 Sun 8.00 - 9.00
Services: Credit cards.

The bookstall on the right as you enter Euston station, stocks
mainly popular paperbacks for the traveller, backed by a few glossy
hardbacks. Also newspapers, records, greeting cards, stationery,
tobacco and confectionery.

ISLAMIC BOOK CENTRE
120 Drummond Street, London NW1 2HL.   **071-388 0710**

Subjects: Islam
Hours: Mon - Sat 10.00 - 6.00.
Services: Mail order, catalogue, special orders, educational
              supply.

A religious bookshop for the faithful or curious. The books are well
displayed and a brisk mail order trade supports the business. Books
are in English, Arabic and other languages of the Moslem world.

W.H. SMITH LTD.
St Pancras Station, London NW1 2QL.   **071-837 5703**

Subjects: General.
Hours: Mon - Fri 7.00 am - 8.00 pm. Sat 7.00 - 7.00. Sun 8.00
                - 6.00.
Services: Credit cards.

Mainly paperbacks are sold at this bookstall on St Pancras
Station to accommodate the travellers.

S.P.C.K. BOOKSHOP
Holy Trinity Church,
Marylebone Road, London NW1 4DU.   **071-387 5282**

Subjects: Religion and theology.
Hours: Mon - Thu 9.00 - 5.30. Fri 9.00 - 5.00.
Services: Mail order (London), credit cards, Church and school
                supply.

Holy Trinity Church lost its Parish in 1952 but now houses two
bookshops. The S.P.C.K. Bookshop carries new religious books
across the whole range of Christianity though Church of England
predominates. It is a spacious premises and clearly laid out. There
is parking space at the front of the shop.

CHARLES HIGHAM
Holy Trinity Church,
Marylebone Road, London NW1 4DU.   **071-387 5282**

Subjects: Antiquarian and secondhand theological books.
Hours: Mon - Thu 9.00 - 5.30. Fri 9.00 - 5.00
Services: Credit cards, mail order.

This is the secondhand and antiquarian department of S.P.C.K.
Bookshop, run as a separate business. The stock of 35,000 books
are in wooden shelves either side of the aisle and near the altar are
the antiquarian books in showcases and glassfronted shelves. All the
books are arranged by subject and there is a comprehensive range
with books in foreign languages included. In the basement are a
further 10,000 titles which is the replacement stock. Parking at the
front.

THE BUSINESS BOOKSHOP
72 Park Road,
London NW1 4SH.

081-723 3902
Fax 071-706 1127

Subjects: Business.
Hours: Mon - Fri 9.00 - 5.30. Tue 9.30 - 5.30. Sat 9.00 - 1.00.
Services: Special orders.

The Business Bookshop is one of the most specialised suppliers of business titles in the U.K. and is particularly strong in the areas of management, marketing, advertising and professional directories. The shop prides itself on a high level of customer service with an exceptionally quick ordering service. It also offers list-building and research facilities. It is part of the Hatchards group.

AL-NOOR BOOKSHOP
54 Park Road, London NW1 4SH.

081-723 5414

Subjects: Islam.
Hours: Mon - Sat 10.00 - 7.00.
Services: Special orders, mail order.

Situated midway between Baker Street tube and the Regent's Park Mosque, this bookseller and publisher stocks books on Islam in English, Arabic and Urdu as well as some interesting non-book material, including the entire Qur'an on cassette with English translation, samples of Islamic calligraphy and jewellery.

METHODIST MISSIONARY SOCIETY BOOKSHOP
25 Marylebone Road, London NW1 5JR.　　**071-935 2541**

Subjects: Religion.
Hours: Mon - Fri 9.00 - 5.00.
Services: Mail order, special orders for religious books.

The Society's shop is in a large premises opposite Madame Tussauds, at street level. The books are mainly Evangelical Christianity with much emphasis on the Third World, hunger and underdevelopment.

DAR AL TAQWA LTD.
7a Melcombe Street, Baker Street, London NW1 6AE. 071-935 6385

Subjects: Islam, Sufism, books in Arabic and English.
Hours: Mon - Sat 9.00 - 6.00.
Services: Special orders (within subject range), mail order, catalogue, credit cards.

This bookshop's speciality is Islamic studies with books in both Arabic and English. The books in Arabic are downstairs and the English ones on the ground floor. Sufism is an important section, the Qur'an is available in many languages and there is a children's section. Also in stock are language dictionaries in Arabic, Persian and Turkish and there is an ELT section for students from Arabic-speaking countries. They are publishers of Islamic books on a wide range of subjects and stock Islamic crafts, clothing, videos and cassettes.

ARCHIVE BOOKSTORE
83 Bell Street, London NW1 6TB. 071-402 8212

Subjects: Antiquarian, secondhand, general, sheet music.
Hours: Mon - Sat 10.00 - 6.00.
Services: Books bought, collections valued.

There is wide general range of books here with classic texts in most subjects, a large section of secondhand sheet music and a bargain stall outside every day. The books are all very reasonably priced and range from 25p to 25. Ideal for lunchtime browsers and those who enjoy a good rummage around.

STEPHEN FOSTER
95 Bell Street, London NW1 6TL. 071-724 0876

Subjects: Art, illustrated, literature, topography, general secondhand and antiquarian.
Hours: Mon - Sat 10.00 - 6.00.
Services: Books bought, book search, special orders (new books), credit cards.

Just off Lisson Grove, Bell Street has had bookshops since the Second World War and this bookshop was formerly owned by P.J.

Cassidy. The books range from secondhand at 50p through to antiquarian. Marylebone and Edgware tube stations are less than a five-minute walk away.

RUDOLF STEINER BOOKSHOP
35 Park Road, London NW1 6XT.   **071-723 4400**

Subjects: Rudolf Steiner, anthroposophical, Waldorf education,
Hours: children's books.
Mon - Fri 10.30 - 2.00, 3.00 - 6.00. Sat 10.30 - 2.00, 3.00 - 5.00.

The bookshop is located in Rudolf Steiner House. Books by Steiner are carried, together with anthroposophical and related general titles, and there is quite a good children's section.

THE FOLK SHOP
Cecil Sharp House,
2 Regent's Park Road, London NW1 7AY.   **071-485 2206**

Subjects: Folk music, folk dance.
Hours: Mon - Fri 9.30 - 5.30.
Services: Mail order, catalogue, library, own magazine.

This large building houses the English Folk Dance and Song Society and downstairs is their bookshop. The books cover the expected range and include some on customs and folk lore; records are also sold.

PENGUIN BOOKSHOP
2 Plaza House, 191 Camden High Street,
London NW1 7BT.   **071-485 1328**

Subjects: General, remainders, Penguins.
Hours: Mon - Sat 9.30 - 6.00. Sun 11.30 - 5.30.
Services: Special orders, credit cards.

A large bookshop opposite Camden Town tube station. The stock is mainly paperback, although there is a comprehensive selection of recent hardbacks at the front of the shop. Every Penguin title available is stocked here and there is a large selection of 'up-market' remainders.

MEGA-CITY COMICS
18 Inverness Street, Camden Town,
London NW1 7HJ.   **071-485 9320**

Subjects: Comics, science-fiction, fantasy and horror.
Hours: Mon - Sun 10.00 - 6.00.
Services: Mail order, comic catalogues, credit cards.

Meg-City Comics is a spacious, colourful shop just off Camden
High Street, half a minute from Camden Town tube station. The
shop specialises in back-issues of American comics, with over a
hundred thousand in stock. New imports are air-freighted weekly.
The shop also stocks a wide range of graphic novels, newspaper
strip reprints, underground and adult comics, film and horror
magazines, as well as T-shirts, badges and posters. The book
department has an extensive selection of British and American
science-fiction, horror and fantasy paperbacks, fantasy art books,
and body art and tattoo books.

EAST ASIA BOOKSHOP
103 Camden High Street,   **071-388 5783**
London NW1 7JN.   **Fax 071-387 5766**

Subjects: Alternative medicine, natural health, all topics relating to
             health and cookery, Oriental philosophy and living.
Hours: Mon - Sat 10.00 - 5.30.
Services: Mail order, catalogues, credit cards.

The East Asia Bookshop specialises in holistic health and living. The
books are of general interest whereas the adjacent AcuMedic Centre,
with which it is associated, stocks professional publications, both
alternative and orthodox.

ACUMEDIC CENTRE
101 Camden High Street,   **071-388 6704**
London NW1 7JN.   **Fax 071-387 5766**

Subjects: Professional textbooks on acupuncture, Chinese
             medicine, homeopathy, herbalism, osteopathy, some
             orthodox medical textbooks.
Hours: Mon - Sat 10.00 - 5.30.
Services: Credit cards, mail order, catalogues.

The books here are professional textbooks for various branches of alternative medicine. Educational materials such as videos, charts and other supplies relating to to these are also available.

REGENT BOOKSHOP
73 Parkway, London NW1 7PP.   **071-485 9822**

Subjects: General.
Hours: Mon - Sat 9.00 - 6.30, Sun 12.00 - 4.00 (flexible).
Services: Special orders.

Bright as a new pin, with good general stock and aiming to keep all Penguin and Pelican books. They are willing to order books not in stock for their customers. A point of light in a postal district rather thin on good general bookshops.

SKOLA BOOKS
27 Delancey Street, Regents Park,   **071-388 0632**
London NW1 7RX.   **071-387 0656**

Subjects: English language teaching, education.
Hours: Mon - Fri 1.00 - 3.00 plus other times in office hours.
Services: Mail order, school, college supply, Eng. lang. library.

An office as well as a shop because most business is mail order but visitors are welcome especially between one o'clock and three, and at other times for serious customers. They specialise in educational books and have a small selection of dictionaries, both English and foreign. You will find here all the revision books for schools and for adult language courses running through all the stages of general education. A specialist E.L.T. library is housed at one of their associated schools, at 21 Star Street, London W2 1QB.

WALDEN BOOKS
38 Harmood Street, London NW1 8DP.   **071-267 8146**

Subjects: General, literature, art (secondhand).
Hours: Thu - Sun 10.30 - 6.30.
Services: Books bought.
A little off the beaten track and with rather odd opening hours. The books are arranged by subject and there is a section of good quality paperbacks, with an additional display on the pavement.

OFFSTAGE
37 Chalk Farm Road,
Camden Town, London NW1 8JA.   **071-485 4996**

Subjects: New and secondhand books on theatre, cinema, T.V. and dance.
Hours: Mon 10.00 - 5.00. Tue - Sat 10.00 - 5.30. Sun 11.00 - 6.00.
Services: Mail order, catalogue, special orders, credit cards.

This unusual bookshop concentrates on all aspects of theatre and cinema, including theatre in education. Literary criticism, biographies and stagecraft are well represented and there are sections on puppetry and magic. An ever-changing selection of memorabilia, a large collection of old programmes backed by postcards and posters make this bookshop well worth a visit.

THE MUSTARD SEED
21 Kentish Town Road, London NW1 8NH.   **071-267 5646**

Subjects: Christian apologetics and the creation debate.
Hours: Mon - Sat 11.00 - 7.00.
Services: Mail order, exhibitions.

A small bookshop one minute from Camden Town tube station. It is often mistaken for a plant shop because of the horticultural interests of the owner. Specialises in Christian apologetics and in particular the debate about the origin of life and of the universe - whether it is the product of design or of random evolution.

Most C.S. Lewis titles are kept in stock and there is a selection of recorded talks on cassettes dealing with apologetics and the creation debate and related subjects.

COMPENDIUM BOOKSHOP
234 Camden High Street,   **071-267 1525**
London NW1 8QS.   **071-485 8944**

Subjects: General, politics, psychology, music, alternative technologies, feminism and gay books, travel.
Hours: Mon - Sat 10.00 - 6.00. Sun 11.00 - 5.00.
Services: Special orders, mail order, catalogues, journal subscription.
There is plenty of room to browse among the sections on psychology, alternative medicines and politics in this bookshop in Camden Town. It is quite a surprise to find two large floors with striped wood shelves holding a great variety of new books. They

cover all the general subjects but specialise in many; art, music, drama, philosophy, politics, education, and psychology. There are also good selections under religion combined with the occult, health, healing, food and nutrition, organic gardening, alternative technologies, urban studies, feminist and gay books and their range is very much wider than the average bookshop. There is a noticeboard advertising events related to their specialist subjects.

PRIMROSE HILL BOOKS
134 Regents Park Road, London NW1 8XL.   **071-586 2022**

Subjects: General, new and secondhand.
Hours: Mon - Sun 10.00 - 6.00.
Services: Credit cards, magazine subscriptions, photocopying, special orders, book tokens.

This shop is recognised by its attractive royal blue exterior and awning. Inside the entrance is the new stock, hard and soft backed, covering a wide range of subjects. Down a spiral staircase are the secondhand books burgeoning from shelves and flowing on to the carpet, arranged by subject and including books on art, history, English and French literature and philosophy. Literary magazines and cards are also stocked. A most interesting shop between high bourgeois Regents Park and throbbing Camden Town.

GABRIEL'S BOOKSHOP
47 Walm Lane, London NW2 4QU.   **081-451 2047**

Subjects: General, Spain, educational books.
Hours: Mon - Sat 10.00 - 6.30.
Services: Educational supply, book exchange service, Spanish spoken.

The shop specializes in new Spanish books for schools and colleges and stocks a good supply of these. This interesting shop next to Willesden Green station is also packed with general secondhand fiction, with bargain trays outside the shop. Non-fiction is kept at the rear of the shop, together with more valuable items of stock. An interesting place where 'finds' might be made.

W.H. SMITH LTD.
82 Walm Lane, London NW2 4RA.   **081-459 0455**

Subjects: General.
Hours: Mon - Sat 8.30 - 6.00.
Services: Special orders, credit cards.

If you want to buy a book in these parts this is where you will probably go. A fairly small general range of books is held in stock.

HIMALAYA BOOKS
Park Publications, 1 Park Close,
London NW2 6RQ.   **081-452 4182**

Subjects: Books from India on all subjects.
Hours: Mon - Sat 9.00 - 6.00.
Services: Mail order, library supply.

Himalaya Books, an associate company of Park Publications, is predominantly a mail order service but potential customers are welcome to call. They specialise in books on Hinduism, Sikhism, yoga, Indian cookery, astrology, palmistry, Asian languages and dictionaries, and autobiographies. They also publish a quarterly news magazine, *India - Home and Abroad.*

KEITH FAWKES
1-3 Flask Walk, London NW3 1HJ.   **071-435 0614**

Subjects: Antiquarian and secondhand.
Hours: Mon - Sat 10.00 - 5.30.
Services: Books may be mailed on request.

White painted brick with green painted windows and door describes
the shop front at One to Three Flask Walk. In three windows a
representative selection of secondhand and out of print books, both
recent and antiquarian, is displayed. Inside you are greeted by rows
of shelves in corridors filled with books on various subjects. Up a
few steps into what used to be the next door shop are more
secondhand books and a narrow room of antiquarian books
sectioned off. This is the specialist stock of rare English and foreign
books. There is often an excellent selection of sheet music and the
shop is proud of its large paperback section. An interesting shop,
which is well organised, considering the range and variety of books.

WATERSTONE'S BOOKSELLERS
68-69 Hampstead High Street, London NW3 1QP. 071-794 1098

Subjects: General.
Hours: Mon - Fri 10.00 - 9.00. Sat 10.00 - 8.00. Sun 11.00 - 7.00.
Services: Special orders, mail order, school and library supply, out
of print book search, credit cards.

The two spacious floors at Waterstone's in Hampstead carry an
enormous stock in many general subjects. Its fiction section is
among the largest in London and includes a good selection of works
in translation, as well as a selection of foreign-language novels from
the continent. The children's section on the first floor is pleasant
and airy, and offers books for all ages up to fourteen years. The
staff in all departments are knowledgeable and maintain the stock
themselves.

THE BELSIZE BOOKSHOP
193 Haverstock Hill, London NW3 4QG.   **071-794 4006**

Subjects: General.
Hours: Mon - Fri 9.30 - 6.30, Sat 9.30 - 5.30.
Services: Special orders, college supply.

Bright, but traditional, the Belsize Bookshop covers most subjects expected of a general bookshop. There are many cases and stands stocking new hardbacks and paperbacks. Themes popular in the district are well covered such as art and travel and there is a good selection of children's books. The shop is well organised, subjects are clearly marked and it has an inviting atmosphere, as befits a shop in one of London's more attractive 'villages'.

VILLAGE BOOKSHOP
46 Belsize Lane, London NW3 5AR.   **071-794 3180**

Subjects: Antiquarian, Secondhand, Germany, travel.
Hours: Mon - Sat 11.00 - 5.30.

Once the Rosslyn Hill Bookshop but now moved to Belsize Village. Every inch of this shop is crammed with books and the German section, with books in German and on Germany, is impressive. There are no new books here but the range of titles and prices is wide; a good collector's hunting ground.

FITZJOHNS BOOKS
27a Northways Parade, College Crescent,
Swiss Cottage, London NW3 5DN.   **071-722 9864**

Subjects: General, secondhand and antiquarian.
Hours: Mon - Sat 11.00 - 5.00.
Services: Books purchased.

An interesting, tight little secondhand bookshop with a good range of general titles as well as scholarly and academic remainders and some sheet music. Only a few minutes' walk from Swiss Cottage tube, but note the address as it is easily missed in passing.

H. KARNAC (BOOKS) LTD.
118 Finchley Road, London NW3 5HJ.   071-431 1075

Subjects: Psychoanalysis, psychotherapy, analytical psychology, general.
Hours: Mon - Sat 9.00 - 6.00.
Services: Special orders.

An appropriate location for this new branch of the well-known Gloucester Road shop. The specialist stock covers psychoanalysis, psychotherapy, social work and counselling, and includes their own 'Maresfield Library' and 'Karnac Books' imprints. A good general range of books complements the specialist ones, and layout and display is excellent.

VICTORY BOOKSHOP
339 Finchley Road, London NW3 6EP.   071-794 7353

Subjects: Christian literature.
Hours: Mon - Fri 9.30 - 5.00. Sat 10.00 - 4.00.
Services: Special orders, mail order, catalogue, credit cards.

The spacious bookshop fronting the Hampstead Bible School's premises in Finchley Road stocks predominantly paperback titles relating to their particular approach to Christianity. A good proportion are US publications. They have a large stock of Bibles and children's books as well as instructional materials, some of which tie in with the range of Christian videos, tapes and records which they also sell.

W.H. SMITH LTD.
9-10 Harben Parade, Finchley Road,
London, NW3 6JS.   071-722 4441

Subjects: General.
Hours: Mon - Sat 9.00 - 6.00.
Services: Credit cards, special orders.

Quite a well stocked shop with a table of bargain books.

PARAPHERNALIA
2 Midland Crescent,
Finchley Road, London NW3 6NP.   **071-435 4634**

Subjects: Science fiction, horror (paperback and secondhand)
Hours: Mon - Sat 10.30 - 7.00.
Services: Special orders.

This small shop is in the precinct of the old Frognal and Finchley Road Station. Besides Sci-fi and horror, they have titles on romantic fiction and some theatrical books. They also offer a range of computer services — i.e. word processing, catalogues and graphics, and will catalogue private collections of comics, stamps, models etc.

THE LIBRARY BOOKSHOP
Westfield College, Kidderpore Avenue,   **071-790 7911**
London NW3 7ST.   **Fax 071-794 2173**

Subjects: English and American literature, literary criticism, poetry, drama, history, history of art, European literature (French, German and Spanish texts).
Hours: Mon - Fri 9.30 - 5.30.
Services: Special orders, mail order, production of subject catalogues of new books.

This college bookshop is part of Library Book Services Ltd., a company supplying academic and research libraries in Europe. The stock comprises mainly books relating to undergraduate courses taught at Westfield College and, in the summer, books for Open University courses. The bookshop is located at the front of the college library and is open to the public throughout the year.

C AND L BOOKSELLERS
13 Sentinel Square, Brent Street,
London NW4 2FR.   **081-202 5301**

Subjects: General.
Hours: Mon - Sat 9.00 - 5.30
Services: Credit cards, Special orders.

This is quite a good general bookshop located in the small pedestrian square near Tesco's the supermarket. All the books are located on the one floor, with a 'hobbies' and 'childrens' section prominent.

W.H. SMITH LTD.
Brent Cross Shopping Centre,
London NW4 3FB.   **081-202 4226**

Subjects: General.
Hours: Mon - Fri 10.00 - 8.00. Sat 9.00 - 6.00.
Services: Special orders, credit cards.

One of the élite W.H.S. branches, with a greater variety of fiction than any other in London. The staple of light and leisure reading is supplemented by good sections on poetry, travel, business and management, and educational subjects. The book department shares the upper floor with the travel department. In season there is even a foreign language section for visitors.

JOHN LEWIS BRENT CROSS
Brent Cross Shopping Centre, London NW4 3FL.   **081-202 6535**

Subjects: Children's.
Hours: Mon - Fri 10.00 - 8.00. Sat 9.00 - 4.30.

Books and story tapes for children of pre-school age and up to seven years are to be found in the toy department on the first floor. There is ample car parking and adjacent shopping plus a free-flow, self-service restaurant. The store is a branch of the John Lewis Partnership.

FENWICK LTD.
Brent Cross Shopping Centre,
London NW4 3FN   **081-202 8200**

Subjects: Children's.
Hours: Mon - Fri 10.00 - 8.00. Sat 9.00 - 6.00.
Services: Credit cards.

The children's book department is situated on the first floor in the toy department.

FACULTY BOOKS
Middlesex Polytechnic,
The Burroughs, London NW4 4BT.   **081-202 3593**

Subjects: Business studies, law, catering and course-related books.
Hours: Mon, Wed, Fri 10.00 - 4.00. Tue, Thu 10.00 - 6.30.
Services: Special orders, project binding.

The shop is in the grounds of Middlesex Polytechnic but is open to the general public. The service is knowledgeable and swift. The stock is course related and non-fictional. There is also a selection of inexpensive stationery.

HELLENIC BOOKSERVICE
91 Fortess Road, London NW5 1AG.   **071-267 9499**

Subjects: Greece and the Islands, including Cyprus, Turkey (new, secondhand and antiquarian).
Hours: Mon - Sat 9.30 - 6.00.
Services: Special orders, mail order, catalogue, university and library supply, subscriptions to magazines, book launches.

Recently moved from Charing Cross Road to these spacious new premises on two floors. Every subject connected with Greece — its history, language and culture — has its place, and there is also a shelf of Latin classics and a section on Turkish travel and archeology. The shop is something of a centre for the Greek community in London for whom it stocks general and children's books in Greek and also sells Greek newspapers.

BELLMAN BOOKSHOP
155 Fortess Road, London NW5 2HR.   **071-485 6698**

Subjects: Marxist, English literature, politics and history.
Hours: Mon - Sat 10.00 - 5.00. Wed closed.
Services: Mail order, special orders, subscriptions to 'The Worker'.

Marxist literature appears to be the main theme but other subjects such as health, hobbies, history, general interest books on Britain and children's books are available in a very roomy and sparsely furnished shop where browsers are welcome, if not converted. There is also a small section of secondhand paperbacks.

OWL BOOKSHOP
211 Kentish Town Road, London NW5 2JU.   **071-485 7793**

Subjects: General, humanities, children's.
Hours: Mon - Sat 9.30 - 6.00.
Services: Special orders, school supply, mail order, credit cards.

A very spacious and brightly lit modern bookshop in Kentish Town, well planned with clear section headings. The main stock is general and there are strong sections on literature, history and philosophy. Their large children's section is an additional feature. The friendly staff offer helpful advice and there is easy access for wheelchairs.

ERIC & JOAN STEVENS BOOKSELLERS
74 Fortune Green Road, London NW6 1DS.   **071-435 7545**

Subjects: General, literature, poetry, art, history, politics, feminism (secondhand).
Hours: Sat 10.00 - 5.30 (other days by appointment). Winter 10.00 - 5.00
Services: Mail order, search service, specialist catalogues (feminism, poetry etc.)

As life ebbs away from West End Lane into Fortune Green Road one comes upon this rather marvellous shop, but alas again, open only on Saturdays as a rule. It passes the test of the aficionado by smelling right to start with. Inside its heavily stocked room are thousands of books, mostly secondhand, on literature, poetry, feminism and all manner of things. The shop window, which unless you are forewarned, is all you will see, is festooned with announcements about poetry readings, women's group meetings and other local events.

SWISS COTTAGE BOOKS
4 Canfield Gardens, London NW6 3BS.   **071-625 4632**

Subjects: Fiction, classics, women's fiction, biography, poetry, drama, travel.
Hours: Mon - Sat 9.30 - 6.00.
Services: Credit cards, institutional supply, special orders.

Undeterred by the rise of the multiple bookstores, this small bookshop with its unique mezzanine continues to offer a standard of service and selection in which its owners, Mary Ashenden and Lawrence Cohen, take pride.

CHANGES BOOKSHOP
242 Belsize Road, London NW6 4BT.   **071-328 5161**

Subjects: Psychotherapy, psychology, personal and spiritual development.
Hours: Mon - Fri 10.00 - 6.00. Sat 10.00 - 5.00.
Services: Mail order (lists), bookstalls for conferences and workshops. Tea and coffee free. Toys to keep children amused. Notice board for adverts.

This most unusual bookshop, three minutes' walk, away from Kilburn High Road Station and Kilburn Park tube, specialises in books on psychology and in 'all the dynamic and classical areas of psychotherapy'. This includes Jungian and analytic psychologies, hypnosis/NLP, humanistic psychology, management development, art, music and creative therapies as well as holistic health and healing, acupuncture, spirituality, Eastern religions and astrology. You are made welcome here and with tea or coffee given free, may browse around to find the answer to your problems.

THE KILBURN BOOKSHOP
8 Kilburn Bridge,
Kilburn High Road, London NW6 6HT.   **071-328 7071**

Subjects: General, Ireland, feminism, Black studies, children's.
Hours: Mon - Sat 9.30 - 5.00.
Services: Credit cards, special orders.

As Kilburn High Street is full of unimpressive shops it is a pleasant surprise to find an excellent general bookshop which endeavours to cover most subjects within reason and also stocks new hardback fiction. They have a good feminist section, specialise in Irish books, fiction, history and folk lore and try to cater for the British Black community with books on West Indian culture. Politics with a left wing bias are well covered and supported by a wide range of alternative magazines. They pride themselves on a fast ordering service and stock books on travel and guides, etc. The address is a little difficult to locate: it is opposite Kilburn High Road (British Rail) Station, near Kilburn Park tube.

W.H. SMITH LTD.
113 Kilburn High Road, London NW6 6JH.   **071-328 3111**

Subjects: General.
Hours: Mon - Sat 8.30 - 5.30.
Services: Credit cards, special orders.

A standard W.H.S. with the usual general range of books.

W.H. SMITH LTD.
29 The Broadway, Mill Hill, London NW7 3DA.   **081-959 1316**

Subjects: General.
Hours: Mon - Sat 8.30 - 5.30.
Services: Special orders, credit cards.

The only shop in the immediate vicinity selling books, general, popular and selling well.

GILBERTS BOOKSHOP
H.M.P. Confectioners Ltd.,
26 Circus Road, London NW8 6PD.   **071-722 8863**

Subjects: General.
Hours: Mon - Sat 8.00 - 6.30, Sun 9.00 - 2.00.
Services: Special orders.

In a small parade of shops near Lord's cricket ground, Gilberts have
expanded the book section at the expense of the confectionery and
stationery. Besides fiction in hard and paperback and children's
books, they have non-fiction sections of which sport (naturally),
biography, cookery, travel and reference are the most prominent.

PEREIRA
35 St. John's Wood High Street,
London NW8 7NJ.   **071-722 3815**

Subjects: General.
Hours: Mon - Sat 7.30 - 6.30. Sun 8.30 - 1.30.

Primarily a newsagents and stationers but with a small stock of
general books and quite a good children's section.

ST. JOHNS WOOD NEWSAGENTS
134 St. John's Wood High Street,
London NW8 7SE.   **071-722 8800**

Subjects: General and books in Arabic.
Hours: Mon - Fri 7.30 - 7.30. Sat 8.00 - 6.30. Sun 9.00 - 3.00.
Services: Credit cards, special orders.

This is a busy local newsagent with quite a good stock of general
books including some in Arabic for the local community of visitors
from the Middle East.

CHAPTER TRAVEL
126 St. John's Wood High Street,   **071-722 0722**
London NW8 7ST.   **071-586 9451**

Subjects: Travel, Cookery, Wine, Maps and Guides.
Hours: Mon - Fri 9.30 - 6.00. Sat 9.30 - 1.00.
Services: Travel agents, credit cards, book lists, travel accessories,
              theatre booking agents.

A marvellous shop for the traveller, which not only spans the large range of books, maps and guides but backs this up with the travel agency. The books on continental wines and cooking supplement the travel section to make this a most worthwhile visit for all would be travellers — or armchair dreamers. The Italian section is particularly strong on guides and cook books. The necessary impedimenta sold include, travel plugs, warning triangles for motorists, travel irons and headlamp convertors.

BIBLIOPOLA
Alfie's Antique Market,
13 Church Street, London NW8 8TD.   **071-724 7231**

Subjects: Antiquarian, private presses, modern first editions, children's books.
Hours: Tue - Sat 10.00 - 5.30.
Services: Mail order, search service, lists.

A large room on the first floor of the market, with a good general range of antiquarian, secondhand and illustrated books, all in immaculate condition.

NW9~NW11

THE BOOKSHOP LTD.
207 Edgware Road, London NW9 6LD.   **081-200 0178**

Subjects: Popular, general.
Hours: Mon - Sat 8.00 - 6.00.

A stationers which has space for mainly paperback books of general appeal including Penguins but very much orientated to the light reader.

KINGSBURY STATIONERS
527 Kingsbury Road, London NW9 9EG.   **081-204 7400**

Subjects: General.
Hours: Mon - Fri 6.00 - 6.00. Sat 6.00 - 5.30.

A newsagents and stationers with a selection of popular fiction, mostly paperbacked, childrens books, hobbies, cookery and gardening in stock.

J. AISENTHAL
11 Ashbourne Parade,
Finchley Road, London NW11 0AD.   **081-455 0501**

Subjects: Judaica in Hebrew and English.
Hours: Mon - Thu 9.00 - 6.00. Fri. 9.00 - 3.00. Sun 9.30 - 1.15.
Services: Special orders, book lists.

The spiritual and cultural needs of the large Jewish community around Golders Green are well served by this shop. Besides the texts in English and Hebrew it also sells religious requisites.

W.H. SMITH LTD.
22 Temple Fortune Parade,
London NW11 0QS.   **081-455 2273**

Subjects: General.
Hours: Mon - Sat 9.00 - 6.00.
Services: Special orders, credit cards.

A limited amount of bookspace at ground level, no other good, general bookshops nearby so we must infer that the trading community is adequately served by this branch of W.H.S..

MARTIN THE NEWSAGENT
26 Market Place, Falloden Way,
London NW11 6JJ.   **081-455 9720**

Subjects: General.
Hours: Mon - Sat 7.30 - 5.30. Sun 7.30 - 1.00 p.m.

The hours here tell their tale, that this is primarily a newsagents with a small section of paperbacks and children's books.

JERUSALEM THE GOLDEN   **081-455 4960**
146-148 Golders Green Road,   **081-458 7011**
London NW11 8HE.   **Fax 081-203 7808**

Subjects: Judaica in Hebrew and English.
Hours: Mon - Thu 9.30 - 6.00. Fri 9.30 - 4.00. Sun 9.30 - 5.00.
Sat closed.
Services: Credit cards, special orders.

Gifts, religious requisites and books fill two small rooms of this shop in Golders Green. The books are selected for adults and children in the Jewish community and have a good selection of Bibles and dictionaries as part of their religious and educational sections. Their selection of Hebrew and Jewish records, cassettes and videos is the largest in Europe. There are paintings of Israel and Jewish subjects and a collection of silverware.

LAVELLS
38-40 Golders Green Road, London NW11 8LL.   **081-458 5691**

Subjects: General.
Hours: Mon - Fri 7.30 - 7.00. Sat, Sun 8.00 - 5.30.
Services: Special orders, credit cards.

This is a large stationers with some books of general appeal. If you have a hobby, want a guide book of London or want to check whether the book is as good as the T.V. serial, there is no reason to go any further.

W.H. SMITH LTD.
889 Finchley Road, Golders Green,
London NW11 8RR.   081-455 0036

Subjects: General.
Hours: Mon - Sat 8.30 - 5.30.
Services: Special orders, credit cards.

The whole of the first floor of this shop sells books and it has a
children's corner, and tables with guides and dictionaries. With
dentists to the north of them, doctors to the south and a screen of
innumerable vets surrounding, Golders Green serves the reading
habits of the professional classes hereabouts and they don't seem to
vary much from those of the quantity surveyors, auctioneers and
structural engineers farther to the north in Muswell Hill.

MENORAH PRINT AND GIFT SHOP
227 Golders Green Road, London NW11 9ES.   081-458 8289

Subjects: Judaica in Hebrew and English.
Hours: Mon - Thu 9.30 - 1.00 p.m. 2.00 - 6.00. Fri 9.00 - 1.00.
              Sun 9.45 - 1.00
Services: Special orders.

A shop with a bright blue front selling books on Jewish themes as
well as gifts and religious artifacts.

LONDON CITY MISSION
175, Tower Bridge Road, London SE1 2AH.　　　**071-407 7585/7**

Subjects:　Christian literature.
Hours:　Mon - Fri 9.30 - 5.00.
Services:　Special orders, Bible readings, missionary supply.

Just south of Tower Bridge is a modern building housing the
London City Mission and the reception area is made over to their
bookshop with tables displaying their Christian literature.
Downstairs there are more tables of books and a book room with
their stock of Bibles and other religious subjects — all open to the
public and of particular interest to people attending the meetings
and Bible readings.

THE RIVERSIDE BOOKSHOP LTD.
Hay's Galleria, London Bridge City,
Tooley Street, London SE1 2HN.　　　**071-378 1824**

Subjects:　General, travel, business.
Hours:　Mon - Fri 9.30 - 6.00. Sat, Sun 12.00 - 5.30.
Services:　Credit cards, special orders.

Beautifully located in one of London's most prestigious
refurbishments, the former Hay's Wharf, which now offers an
attractive blend of shops and restaurants. Serving both the on-site
business community and visitors, The Riverside Bookshop has
successfully established itself in the area.

DENNYS BOOKSELLERS LTD.
62-64 Weston Street, London SE1 3QJ.　　　**071-378 7834**

Subjects:　Medical, general, (new and secondhand).
Hours:　Mon - Fri 9.30 - 6.00. Occasional Sats.
Services:　Credit cards, special order, mail order (list, catalogues)

This bookshop is located opposite Guys hospital. The medical
section is extensive, ranging from scientific to technical, but there is
still room for general remainders and some reference books. On the
lower ground floor is a wide range of secondhand medical books.

IMPERIAL WAR MUSEUM SHOP
Lambeth Road, London SE1 6HZ.   **071-735 8922**

Subjects: Wars from 1914 onwards.
Hours: Mon - Sun 10.00 - 6.00.
Services: Mail order, lists of own publications, credit cards.

A spacious shop inside the War Museum with new hardback and paperback books mainly on the two World Wars. The books are on tables or shelves under subject with the Museum's own publications being one of their specialities.

PARKS
Academic & Professional Books,   **071-928 5378**
18 London Road, London SE1 6JX.   **Fax 071-261 9536**

Subjects: Computing, business and social sciences.
Hours: Mon - Fri 9.00 - 6.00.
Services: Special orders, mail order, free annual computing catalogue with monthly updates, library supply.

One of London's leading computing bookshops, it combines a wide stock range with fast order facilities. Elephant & Castle is the nearest tube station.

THE COLLEGE BOOKSHOP
London College of Printing, Elephant and Castle,
London SE1 6SB.   **071-735 8570**

Subjects: Printing and graphic design.
Hours: Mon - Fri 10.15 - 1.30, 2.30 - 5.30 (Term time only).
Services: Special orders.

Upstairs, opposite the main entrance is the college bookshop which sells books on printing and graphic design over a counter — no browsing here but books may be examined at the counter.

W.H. SMITH LTD.
Elephant & Castle Shopping Centre,
London SE1 6SZ.   **071-703 8525/6**

Subjects: General.
Hours: Mon - Sat 8.30 - 5.30 (Tue 9.30 - 5.30)
Services: Credit cards, special orders.

It is a relief to see the familiar, well lit, well organised W.H. Smith cheer up this dismal shopping centre at the Elephant and Castle. Books have most of the top floor to themselves except for the travel section. An escalator outside can take you to this level and general subjects are covered with the usual glossy present books available and a good educational section. This is the only bookshop in the centre so their ordering service must be welcome to the local population.

THE BOOKSHOP
4, Kennington Road, London SE1 7BL.   **071-261 1385**

Subjects: General.
Hours: Mon - Fri 10.00 - 5.30.
Services: Special orders. Credit cards.

A good, small general bookshop with predominantly paperbacks but the hard backed section is expanding. The reference and non-fiction section is substantial as is the children's section. There is a rapid ordering service.

DILLONS THE BOOKSTORE
Medical School Library, St. Thomas' Medical School,
Lambeth Palace Road, London SE1 7EH.   **071-928 7926**

Subjects: Medical texts for under- and postgraduates, nursing titles
             and related reading.
Hours: Mon - Fri 11.00 - 2.30.
Services: Special orders, mail order, lists, institutional supply,
             customer accounts, credit cards.

Dillons in St. Thomas' contains similar stock to Dillons in Charing Cross & Westminster Medical School. Previously open only three days each week, the bookstore has begun opening for five days due to demand from the school and other medical institutions.

JOHN MENZIES (G.B.) LTD.
St. Thomas' Hospital, Lambeth Palace Road,
London SE1 7EH.   **071-928 0793**

Subjects: Paperback fiction, health.
Hours: Mon - Fri 7.30 - 7.30. Sat 9.30 - 6.00. Sun 10.00 - 6.00.
Services: Special orders (mainly medical textbooks), credit cards.

Inside the main entrance to the North Wing of St. Thomas' Hospital, this shop in the Menzies chain aims to stock the necessities of life for both patients and staff. There is a small book section which includes a selection of new titles and bestsellers in paperback, maps of London and books on health. Most of the health books are popular publications but there are some medical textbooks. The rest of the store is given over to such useful items as toiletries, stationery, cards and food and drinks.

I.S.O. PUBLICATIONS
137, Westminster Bridge Road,   **071-261 9588**
London SE1 7HR.   **071-261 9179**

Subjects: Militaria.
Hours: Mon - Fri 9.30 - 5.30. Sat 11.00 - 2.00.
Services: Mail order (catalogue), Credit cards, Special orders.

A small shop stuffed with books about things that go bump in the night (laser guided of course). Combat on land, sea and in the air all covered, mostly by hard backed books but some paperbacks and magazines. The company also publishes its own list of specialist military titles including the 'Outlines' series.

IAN ALLAN LTD.
45/46 Lower Marsh, London SE1 7RG.   **071-401 2100**

Subjects: Transport (railways, road, maritime and air), military.
Hours: Mon - Fri 9.00 - 5.30. Sat 9.00 - 5.00.

Although part of the Ian Allen group, they supply books from many other publishers of transport subjects. Models and transport videos are stocked with train videos a speciality.

CHURCH MISSIONARY SOCIETY
157 Waterloo Road, London SE1 8UU.   **071-928 8681**

Subjects: Christian missionary work.
Hours: Mon - Fri 9.15 - 4.30.
Services: Mail order only. No visitors.

A sales and distribution department within the Society's premises with books, cassettes, audio-visual aids and study material concerned with Christian mission world-wide.

MUSEUM OF THE MOVING IMAGE BOOKSHOP
National Film Theatre, South Bank,
London SE1 8XT.   **071-928 3535**

Subjects: Film, TV, media.
Hours: Mon 12.00 - 7.00. Tue - Sat 10.30 - 8.45. Sun & Bank
              Holidays 10.30 - 8.00. (Longer hours on Sunday in
              summer).
Services: Mail order, special orders, college orders, credit cards.

Located near the entrance to the Museum of the Moving Image, the MOMI Bookshop specialises in books on film, TV and media. It has a wide range of books on every aspect of the cinema and TV and carries a small selection of film books in foreign languages. The areas covered include film history, criticism, documentary, biography, genres, history, screen plays, screenwriting, censorship, film guides, technical, special effects, and animation. All BFI publications are either in stock or available within twenty-four hours. Magazines and cards are also sold.

The staff are friendly and helpful and will try to answer customers' queries and give information on film-related subjects.

SHERRATT & HUGHES
The Royal Festival Hall,
South Bank, London SE1 8XX.   **071-620 0403**

Subjects: Music, poetry, art, paperback fiction, general.
Hours: Mon - Sun 11.00 - 10.00.
Services: Mail order, special orders, credit cards.

This bookshop, open seven days a week, is on level 2 just inside the Royal Festival Hall. The main specialisation is in classical music (biographies of composers, technical books etc.) and there is an ever-growing poetry section. Sheet music, scores and recordings are now available from two separate shops also on level 2. They also seem to act as an information centre for the whole area!

THE HAYWARD GALLERY BOOKSHOP
The Hayward Gallery, Belvedere Road,
London SE1 8XZ.   071-928 3144

Subjects: Art.
Hours: Open during gallery hours during exhibitions. (At present
            Mon, Fri, Sat, Sun 10.00 - 6.00. Tue, Wed 10.00 - 8.00).
            Closed during exhibition intervals.
Services: Mail order for South Bank Centre Publications.

The shop specialises in publications relating to exhibitions held at the
gallery. The range of catalogues, books, posters and postcards
includes items from past shows as well as a selection of titles of
general interest on modern art and a small selection of art
magazines.

W.H. SMITH LTD.
Main Line Bookstall,
Waterloo Station, London SE1 9NQ.   071-261 1616

Subjects: General.
Hours: Mon - Fri 7.00 - 9.30. Sat 7.00 - 9.00. Sun 9.00 - 8.00.
Services: Credit cards.

This is the larger bookstall in the centre of Waterloo Station and
holds the usual general subjects including children's books.

W.H. SMITH LTD.
Loop Bookstall,
Waterloo Station, London SE1 9NQ.   071-928 8478

Subjects: General.
Hours: Mon - Fri 7.00 - 7.30.
Services: Credit cards.

On the Windsor line side of Waterloo Station is the shelter bookstall
selling mainly paperbacks — with a few hardback bargains — to
accommodate the travellers.

ROYAL NATIONAL THEATRE BOOKSHOP
Upper Ground, South Bank, London SE1 9PX.   **071-928 2033**

Subjects: Play texts, theatre.
Hours: Mon - Sat 10.00 a.m. - 11.00 p.m. (- 8.00 p.m. when no performance in the Lyttleton Theatre).
Services: Mailing list, mail order (worldwide), telephone order, credit cards.

The bookshop is on the ground floor in the foyer of the Lyttleton Theatre and is surrounded by exhibitions, buffets and bars with seating space. It has probably the longest theatre bookshop opening hours in the country.

It stocks a huge range of titles on all aspects of the theatre, plus magazines, posters, video and audio recordings, cards, gifts and gift tokens. Play texts are arranged alphabetically by author and, for ease, under the theatre at which the play in question is currently running in the West End or elsewhere.

Notably, this bookshop hosts frequent signings by authors from both within and beyond the theatre world. Recent visiting authors include Dirk Bogarde, Kenneth Branagh, Peter Brook, Arthur Miller and Terence Stamp.

W.H. SMITH & SON LTD.
London Bridge, London SE1 9SP.   **071-403 3288**

Subjects: General.
Hours: Mon - Fri 7.00 - 7.30.
Services: Special orders, credit cards.

Situated on London Bridge station, W.H. Smith cater for the popular titles that attract passengers and people with time to kill. Hence the best sellers are backed by the usual gardening and cookery sections.

MARTIN THE NEWSAGENT
20 Tranquil Vale,
Blackheath, London SE3 OAB.   **081-852 0367**

Subjects: Paperback fiction, remainders.
Hours: Mon - Wed 6.00 - 5.30. Thu - Sat 6.00 - 6.00.
Services: Credit cards.

Martin the Newsagent sell some books in their branch in Blackheath, mainly paperback fiction but also a small selection of hardback remainders.

THE BOOKSHOP, BLACKHEATH LTD.
74, Tranquil Vale, London SE3 OBN.   **081-852 4786**

Subjects: General secondhand and antiquarian, some new paperbacks.
Hours: Mon - Sat 9.30 - 5.00 (Closed Thu).
Services: Books bought, scarce and out of print books traced.

None of the usual gloom, dust and disorder that most secondhand bookshops seem to have here. This is a very attractive shop with most of the space taken up by the comprehensive stock of secondhand books and a small area by the door for new paperbacks, including children's. Local history is well represented and includes their own three-volume history of Blackheath. Given the limited space it is rather a clever combination of subjects.

BOOKS OF BLACKHEATH
11, Tranquil Vale,
Blackheath Village, London SE3 OBU.   **081-852 8185**

Subjects: General.
Hours: Mon - Fri 9.30 - 5.30. Sat 9.30 - 5.00.
Services: Special orders.

A small bright shop making the most of limited space. At ground level they have their new stock, grouped by subject and upstairs are books at reduced prices.

STUDIO BOOKS
1st Floor Rear, 2 Montpelier Vale,
Blackheath, London SE3 0TA.   **081-318 9666**

Subjects: General secondhand, some antiquarian, academic
remainders.
Hours: Tue - Sat 11.00 - 6.00.
Services: Books bought.

Access is through an archway and 40 yards along the mews. Among
its specialities this very worthwhile shop includes out of print
technology and medicine, social sciences, sport, detective and
science fiction. There is also a good selection of out of print Pelicans
and Penguin non-fiction.

EUROCENTRE BOOKSHOP
21 Meadow Court Road,
Lee Green, London SE3 9EU.   **081-318 5633**

Subjects: English as a foreign language.
Hours: Mon, Fri 1.00 - 4.30. Tue, Thu 11.00 - 2.15. Wed 1.30
- 2.30

A small room at this centre serves as a bookshop, providing books
for the students but open also to the public, to some of whom
English may well be a foreign language.

CHURCH ARMY RESOURCE CENTRE
Independents Road, London SE3 9LG.   **081-318 1226**

Subjects: Christian literature.
Hours: Mon - Fri 9.00 - 5.00. Sat 10.00 - 12.00.
Services: Special orders, mail order, church and school supply,
credit cards.

The Church Army headquarters are in a private road beside
Blackheath station and accommodate a bookshop on the ground
floor (to the right inside the entrance). Much of their trade is in the
sale and hire of videos and audio-visuals, but the book stock is
substantial and covers a wide area of Christian publishing.

SE5

Camberwell

THE PASSAGE BOOKSHOP
5, Canning Cross, Grove Lane,
Camberwell, London SE5 8BH.　　　　　**071-274 7606**

Subjects: General, medicine, dentistry, nursing.
Hours: Mon - Fri 10.00 - 6.00. Sat 10.00 - 5.00.
Services Credit cards, special orders.

A charming, Dickensian shop, something of a local haunt. It caters for an educated general public as well as for the doctors, psychiatrists, dentists and nurses at the several nearby hospitals. There is also a good children's section and a marvellous selection of unusual cards. Special orders are a strong feature.

STONE TROUGH BOOKS
59 Camberwell Grove, London SE5 8JA.　　　　**071-708 0612**

Subjects: General, secondhand and antiquarian.
Hours: Tue - Sat 10.00 - 1.00, 2.00 - 6.00.
Services Mail order, catalogue.

"Books people like to read" is the idea behind the stock of secondhand and antiquarian books with English literature one of the main subjects and art and travel sections among the favourites. George Ramsden obviously enjoys his days in his bookshop and hand picks his stock rather than buying job lots. He has two rooms on different levels for the customers to browse in.

THE CAMBERWELL BOOKSHOP
28 Camberwell Grove,　　　　　　**(shop) 071-701 1839**
London SE5 8RE.　　　　　　**(evenings) 071-701 3450**

Subjects: General, art, architecture, fine bindings, art periodicals (antiquarian and secondhand).
Hours: Tue - Sat 10.00 - 6.00. Otherwise by appointment.
Services: Bookbinding.

This shop has a general stock of antiquarian and secondhand books with specialisation in the decorative and applied arts for the period 1880-1950, also in architecture and commercial art.

W.H. SMITH LTD.
23, Winslade Way, Catford, London SE6 4JU.   **081-690 1972**

Subjects: General.
Hours: Mon - Sat 9.00 - 5.30 (Tue 9.30 - 5.30)
Services Credit cards, Special orders.

Situated in a shopping precinct this branch of WHS has the familiar character of so many branches with a general stock around the walls and best sellers on tables.

DEPTFORD BOOKSHOP AND LITERACY CENTRE,
55 Deptford High Street, London SE8 4AA.   **081-691 8339**

Subjects: General, gay/lesbian, women's studies, Black fiction and non-fiction, children's anti-racist/anti-sexist books.
Hours: Tue, Wed, Fri & Sat 9.30 - 5.30, Thu 9.30 - 1.30. Closed Mon & Sun.
Services Special orders, story telling, bookstalls, adult literacy classes and author events.

A community bookshop literacy centre, non profit making and run by experienced, enthusiastic staff. On Saturday mornings there are story telling sessions for children. Apart from selling a wide range of paperback books for adults and children they sell cards, book tokens and wrapping paper and organise a wide range of interesting events for children and adults.

THE ARCADE BOOKSHOP
3-4 The Arcade, Eltham High Street,   **081-850 7803**
London SE9 1BE   **081-850 4950**

Subjects: Children's, educational, remainders.
Hours: Mon - Sat 9.00 - 5.30 (Thu 9.00 - 1.00).
Services Special orders, school supply, book parties for schools, author visits, in-school bookshops.

Being located in an arcade allows a large display of remaindered books outside on the pavement. Inside there are sections on cookery and gardening, but this is predominantly a bookshop for children with both fiction and non-fiction in stock. The staff are brimming with enthusiasm and their idea of book parties at schools to lay the seed corm for future readers is a good one.

W.H. SMITH LTD.
92-94, High Street, Eltham, London SE9 1BW.   **081-859 3019**

Subjects: General.
Hours: Mon - Sat 8.30 - 5.30. Tue 9.30 - 5.30.
Services   Special orders, credit cards.

This is a small W.H.S. here in Eltham, Bob Hope's home town but you won't find much else that's Morocco bound. The books are on the first floor with most subjects in stock and a good ordering service. Paperback fiction and new titles are the most in demand.

COFFEEHOUSE BOOKSHOP
139 Greenwich South Street, London SE10 8NX   **081-692 3885**

Subjects: General secondhand.
Hours: Mon - Sat 10.00 - 5.30 (lunch 1.00 - 2.00). Thu closed.
Services: Books bought.

The largely paperback stock is strongest in literature and pop music, although most subjects are represented. Secondhand records and cassettes are also sold.

MAGPIE
87 Blackheath Road, London SE10 8PD.   **081-692 2807**

Subjects: General secondhand.
Hours: Mon - Fri 4.00 - 9.00 (variable). Sat, Sun 11.00 - 8.00.
Services: Books bought, credit cards.

As the owner describes it, 'a fine art junk shop with the emphasis on books'. The stock is mostly non-fictional and a speciality is printed ephemera. Opening hours during the week are usually as above but may vary. If in any doubt it might be advisable to telephone before calling.

BOOK BOAT
(P.O. Box 347), Cutty Sark Gardens,
Greenwich Church Street, London SE10 9DB.   **081-853 4383**

Subjects: Children's books.
Hours: Mon - Sun 10.00 - 5.00. Thu closed.
Services Special orders.

This shop is in fact a boat moored near the Cutty Sark. It is imaginatively arranged and colourfully decorated and would be something of a treat for children taken there.

THE GREENWICH BOOKSHOP
37, King William Walk, London SE10 9HU.   **081-858 5789**

Subjects: General, new and secondhand.
Hours: Mon - Sun 10.30 - 5.30.
Services Credit cards, special orders.

This corner shop in Greenwich, open seven days a week, is strong on local history. There are many visitors to the museum and the Cutty Sark nearby who will find a visit here worthwhile. The general sections are good as are travel and reference.

WOMEN & CHILDREN FIRST BOOKSHOP
16 The Market, Greenwich, London SE10 9HZ.   **081-853 1296**

Subjects: Children's, women's.
Hours: Mon - Sun 10.00 - 5.30.
Services: Special orders, credit cards.

In prime position in the market, the bookshop caters mainly for children and has a small section of literature of interest to women.

MARCET BOOKS
4A Nelson Road, Greenwich, London SE10 9JB.   **081-853 5408**

Subjects: General antiquarian and secondhand.
Hours: Mon - Sun 10.30 - 5.30.
Services Mail order, credit cards, book binding.

An alleyway off the Craft Market is the location for this second-hand bookshop covering most general subjects but with strong art, foreign travel, maritime and architecture sections. Books are well displayed with room for browsers and the out of print and antiquarian sections have some very interesting titles.

ROGERS TURNER BOOKS LTD.
22 Nelson Road, Greenwich, London SE10 9JB.   **081-853 5271**

Subjects: General, antiquarian and secondhand scholarly books.
Hours: Sun - Sat 10.00 - 6.00. Thu 10.00 - 2.00.
Services Credit cards, search service, mail order, catalogues.

You are welcome to browse among the shelves of books but the basis of the business is mail order. Greenwich being popular with tourists, most shops cater for visitors and this one is open every day. Their stock includes many scholarly titles, history of science and some valuable antiquarian volumes.

ANTHONY J. SIMMONDS
Maritime Books, 23 Nelson Road, Greenwich,
London SE10 9JB.   **081-853 1727**

Subjects: New, secondhand and antiquarian books, naval, maritime and voyaging.
Hours: Mon - Sat 10.00 - 6.00.
Services: Mail order, catalogues, special order.

The shop has moved from Greenwich Market to a new high street location within walking distance of both the National Maritime Museum and the Cutty Sark.

SPREADEAGLE BOOKSHOP
8 Nevada Street, London SE10 9JL.   **081-305 1666**

Subjects: Antiquarian and secondhand with emphasis on children's books, theatre, cinema, maritime, art, literature, London and Kent history.
Hours: Mon - Sun 10.00 - 5.30.

Opposite Greenwich Theatre, this shop sells some curios and period costume as well as antiquarian and secondhand books. Next door they sell more books and period furniture, original pictures and prints. Both interesting shops with plenty of scope for the bargain hunter.

SOMA BOOKS LTD.
38 Kennington Lane, London SE11 4LS.　　　　**071-735 2101**

Subjects: South Asia, Africa, the Caribbean, Central, South and Black America, children's, women's studies, race, development and education, general.

Hours: Mon - Fri 9.30 - 5.30. Sat 10.00 - 4.00.

Services: Special orders, mail order lists, library and school supply, exhibitions.

Soma Books has now moved from the Commonwealth Institute and the range of books here has been greatly expanded as a result. Their children's section is particularly strong. It includes books which are anti-racist and anti-sexist, books on humour, information books and dual-text books.

There is a wide selection in the women's studies section and the race, development and education section is also well stocked. Other subjects covered are fiction, poetry, literary criticism, history, politics, sociology, art and music. They also stock a wide range of posters, postcards and greeting cards as well as crafts and artifacts imported from co-operatives, women's organisations and family units in India.

DAYBREAK BOOKS
68 Baring Road, Lee, London SE12 OPS.　　　　**081-857 1188**

Subjects: Christian literature.

Hours: Tue - Sat 9.00 - 1.00. 2.00 - 5.30. Mon closed.

Services Special orders, mail order, book parties.

Established by South Lee Christian Centre, a bright shop on two levels selling and in some cases even giving Evangelical Christian literature, tapes and cassettes. There is also quite a large stock of greetings cards on sale. A novel scheme of theirs is holding 'book parties' in people's homes.

ARMY & NAVY STORES LTD.
45, High Street, Lewisham, London SE13 5JR.   **081-852 4321**

Subjects: General.
Hours: Mon - Thu 9.00 - 5.30. Fri & Sat 9.00 - 6.00.
Services   Special orders, credit cards.

This large department store which dominates the High Street does find a place for a small book department selling the usual general range of hard and paper backed books. Children's books, paperback fiction, reference and leisure are perhaps the most prominent sections.

POPULAR BOOK CENTRE
284 Lewisham High Street, London SE13 6JZ.   **081-690 5110**

Subjects: General, secondhand.
Hours: Mon - Sat 10.00 - 5.30.
Services   Exchange with half price credit.

Mainly paperbacks, some well used as this shop offers an exchange service and has a wide selection of popular books from which to choose. Also collectors' comics.

W.H. SMITH LTD.
The Lewisham Centre, 59, Riverdale,
London SE13 7EP.   **081-318 1316**

Subjects: General.
Hours: Mon - Fri 9.00 - 5.30 (Tue 9.00 - 5.30) Sat 8.30 - 5.30.
Services   Credit cards, special orders.

Books share the space in this one level shop with W.H.S's other usual stock but their space allowance is generous. The general stock is shelved and there are book towers displaying current promotions. The shop was completely refurbished in 1988 and is efficiently air-conditioned for the comfort of the customer.

SHERRATT & HUGHES
Goldsmith's College, Lewisham Way, New Cross,
London SE14 6NW.   **081-469 0262**

Subjects: Academic, arts, humanities, social sciences, fiction.
Hours: Mon - Fri 9.00 - 7.00 (term time) 9.00 - 5.30 (vacations).
Services: Special orders, mail order.

Fully refurbished as Sherratt and Hughes, this college bookshop is mainly geared to college courses in the arts, humanities and social sciences. The sections on education, English and drama are particularly strong with a good range of new authors and classics in the fiction section.

THE BOOKPLACE
13 Peckham High Street, London SE15 5EB.   **071-701 1757**

Subjects: Black literature, children's, local community themes, general.
Hours: Mon - Sat 10.00 - 6.00. Thu closed.
Services: Special orders, mail order.

A non-profit making community bookshop serving the local community. The sections on Black interest and community publications are particularly well-stocked as are the women's and children's sections. There are books of gay and lesbian interest. They run schemes to encourage writing and literacy and publish books by and for people living in the Southwark area.

W.H. SMITH LTD.
Aylesham Centre, Rye Lane,
Peckham, London SE15 5EW.   **071-358 9601**

Subjects: General.
Hours: Mon - Sat 9.00 - 5.30. Tue 9.30 - 5.30.
Services: Special orders, credit cards.

A large W.H.Smith with nearly a third of its floor space devoted to the book department. The usual general range of books is here.

W.H. SMITH LTD.
Surrey Quays Shopping Centre, Redriff Road,
London SE16 1LL.   **071-237 5235**

Subjects: General.
Hours: Mon - Wed 9.30 - 6.00. Thu, Fri 9.00 - 8.00, Sat - 6.00.
Services: Special orders, credit cards.

Situated in the new Surrey Quays Shopping Centre, part of the Docklands development, this W.H. Smith has in stock a general range of books which includes a good paperback fiction section.

LABOUR PARTY BOOKSHOP
150, Walworth Road, London SE17 1JT.   **071-703 0833**

Subjects: Politics, general.
Hours: Mon - Fri 9.30 - 5.15.
Services Mail order, special orders.

The shop is inside the Labour Party H.Q. but has a separate entrance. It stocks books on politics (left of course), trades unions, feminism and a range of biographies and autobiographies of Labour worthies. It also functions as a general bookshop , stocking fiction, non-fiction and children's books, mainly paperbacks but also some hardbacks.

W.H. SMITH LTD.
68-72 Powis Street, Woolwich, London SE18 6LQ.   **081-854 7108**

Subjects: General.
Hours: Mon - Fri 8.45 - 5.30. Sat 8.30 - 5.30.
Services: Special orders, telephone credit card orders.

One of the larger W.H. Smith branches which has recently been modernised. Books share the first floor with the travel department and there is plenty of room to walk around.

MERCURY BOOKSHOP
Thames Polytechnic, Wellington Street,
London SE18 6PF.   **081-317 0646**

Subjects: General, academic.
Hours: Mon - Fri 8.45 - 5.30. Wed 8.45 - 5.00.
Services Special orders.

Although attached to the Polytechnic this bookshop has its own wide frontage to Wellington Street and is therefore used by the public for general books. Its main stock, however, is student textbooks: business, all branches of engineering, computing and the social sciences are the principal fields. There is also a popular children's section.

SE20~SE27

Penge - East Dulwich - Dulwich Village - Forest Hill - Herne Hill - Brixton (East) - South Norwood - Sydenham - West Norwood

FOSTICKS
131, High Street, Penge, London SE20 7DS.   **081-778 8265**

Subjects: General.
Hours: Mon - Sat 6.30 - 5.30.
Services Special orders.

The early opening hours denote the fact that this is a newsagents with stationery and confectionery, but they do stock books of popular appeal plus study aids, atlases, maps and guides and a small children's section.

THE ART STATIONERS
31, Dulwich Village, London SE21 7BN.   **081-693 5938**

Subjects: Art and graphics, children's.
Hours: Mon - Sat 9.00 - 5.30.
Services Special orders, credit cards.

Books find a place here in a shop which is dominated by large toys and art materials. A speciality of the shop is pictorial historical guides to the area.

THE GALLERY BOOK SHOP
1d, Calton Avenue, Dulwich Village,
London SE21 7DE.   **081-693 2808**

Subjects: General, children's.
Hours: Mon - Sat 9.30 - 5.30.
Services Special orders, credit cards, school supply.

An attractive blue and white fronted shop, brimming with books on two floors. Downstairs are new titles and fiction, upstairs non-fiction. The children's section in particular is extensive and excellent, those on travel and cookery likewise.

M. & J. COLLINS LTD.
84, Park Hall Road, Dulwich, London SE21 8BW.   081-670 0044

Subjects: General.
Hours: Mon - Sat 9.00 - 1.00, 2.00 - 5.30.
Services Special orders.

Mainly a stationers and printers but with a small selection of books on a few general subjects, reference and dictionaries among them.

DULWICH BOOKS
6, Croxted Road, Dulwich, London SE21 8SW.   081-670 1920

Subjects: General, academic, children's.
Hours: Mon - Sat 9.30 - 5.30. Wed 9.30 - 12.30.
Services Special orders, credit cards.

Expert staff are on hand to guide and their bibliographical resources are available whether you intend to buy or not. The travel section, divided between the places to go and travellers who have been there, is particularly good and includes an extensive range of British and European maps. Children's books comprise the largest section, reference, art and architecture are also strong, and books for all Open University courses are stocked. Computerised ordering makes it possible for them to deal rapidly with customers' requests.

CHENER BOOKS
14 Lordship Lane, East Dulwich,
London SE22 8HN.   071-229 0771

Subjects: General and academic, new and secondhand.
Hours: Mon - Sat 10.00 - 6.00.
Services Credit cards, special orders, mail order, Open University stockists.

An orderly general bookshop designed to provide 'a reasonable alternative to the Central London shops'. The fiction section, including science fiction, is excellent, and history, travel and biography are also well represented. They are stockists for the Open University, and also engage in publishing on their own account, producing titles on local history and of local interest.

W.H. SMITH LTD.
Forest Hill Station, Devonshire Road,
London SE23 3HD. **081-699 2789**

Subjects: General.
Hours: Mon - Sat 8.30 - 5.30. Tue 9.30 - 5.30.
Services Special orders, credit cards.

A first floor divided between records and books with a table of bargain books. Plenty of space.

121 BOOKSHOP & ANARCHIST CENTRE
121 Railton Road, Brixton, London SE24 0LR. **071-274 6655**

Subjects: Anarchism, anarcho-syndicalism, feminism.
Hours: Mon - Sat 1.00 - 5.00. Sun 3.00 - 5.00.

This bookshop stocks about 1,500 titles on anarchism, feminism and related subjects.

AMBASSADOR CHRISTIAN BOOKSHOP
Portland Road,
South Norwood, London SE25 4PN. **081-656 0189**

Subjects: Christian books.
Hours: Mon - Fri 9.15 - 5.00. Sat. 9.15 - 4.00.
Services Special orders, church book stalls, mail order (on monthly sale or return) church supply.

Parking is provided for this bookshop in Portland Road, so look for the junction of Werndee Road as the shop is not numbered. It is bright and roomy with records and tapes available as a back-up for their well displayed stock of Christian books.

SPURGEONS BOOK ROOM
Spurgeons College, 189 South Norwood Hill,
London SE25 6DJ **081-653 3640**

Subjects: Christian and anthropology books.
Hours: Mon - Fri 9.30 - 5.00. Mon, Tue 7.00 - 9.00 (evenings, termtime).
Services: Special orders, credit cards.

Take the South Norwood entrance to the college and there are directions to their bookshop. The general public are welcome and subjects are clearly marked.

KIRKDALE BOOKSHOP
272, Kirkdale, Sydenham, London SE26 4RS.   **081-778 4701**

Subjects: General, new and secondhand.
Hours: Mon - Sat 9.00 - 5.30. Wed closed.
Services   Special orders, books bought, mail order, library and school supply.

This shop, under the same ownership for over 20 years is, once entered rather impressive. On the ground floor are the new titles and general stock and downstairs a good secondhand section and some remainders.

HILLYERS   **081-778 6361**
301 Sydenham Road, London SE26 5EW.   evenings **081-778 6361**

Subjects: General secondhand.
Hours: Mon - Fri 8.30 - 4.00. Sat 8.30 - 2.00. Wed closed.
Services: Books bought.

A long-established firm dealing in antiques and books and stocking about 5,000 general titles.

PAGES BOOK SHOP
22 Knights Hill, West Norwood,
London SE27 0HY.   **081-670 2107**

Subjects: General.
Hours: Mon - Sat 9.30 - 5.30. Longer opening hours in December including Sun.
Services: Special orders with publishers in stock.

A general bookshop offering a broad selection of subjects including fiction, biography, cookery, children's, health, reference, travel, philosophy, psychology, crime, occult, classics, and women's literature. The nearest railway station is West Norwood.

BOOKS, ETC.
66-74 Victoria Street, London SW1A 5LB.   **071-931 0677**

Subjects: General.
Hours: Mon, Tue, Fri 8.30 - 6.30. Wed, Thu 8.30 - 7.00. Sat
Services: 9.30 - 6.30.
Special orders, credit cards, international mail order,
entire shop accessible to wheelchairs.

This spacious and fully air-conditioned shop is only a short distance
from Victoria Station. There is a wide range of both hardback and
paperback, fiction and non-fiction, a well stocked children's
department and a colourful card and gift-wrap section. There is
ample room to browse among the excellent selection of titles in all
the general subjects. The travel department is paticularly good. An
enthusiastic and helpful staff.

BERGER & TIMS
7 Bressenden Place,   **071-828 8322**
London SW1E 5DE   **Fax 071-976 5976**

Subjects: General, politics, literature, travel, gardening, reference,
business, David & Charles publications.
Hours: Mon - Fri 9.00 - 6.00.
Services: Government, public and commercial library supply,
special orders, mail order, credit cards.

Two minutes' walk from Victoria Station, this airy, modern
bookshop has experienced and helpful staff. The wide range of
fiction and non-fiction titles reflects the library supply role of the
company and particularly its government and parliamentary
interests. Reference and travel are strongly featured. There is an
extensive selection of David and Charles books as the shop is their
London stockist. They pride themselves on their highly efficient
mail order service which can be contacted by telephone or fax. Any
British book in print can be obtained quickly and dispatched worldwide. United States publications may also be ordered. There are no
extra charges, apart from postage, for these services.

ARMY & NAVY STORES
P.O. Box 189,   **071-834 1234**
101 Victoria Street, London SW1E 6QX.   **Extn 2105**

Subjects: General, travel, B.B.C. publications, children's.
Hours: Mon - Sat 9.30 - 6.00.
Services: Credit cards, mail order, special orders.

This well known department store has a large book section on its second floor which is excellent in its range and arrangement. The paper and hard backed sections are equally balanced and the titles are arranged by subject and displayed on shelves, tables and stands. There is an extensive children's section including a mini-paperback shelf. This department is better than many shops in London which sell books exclusively.

COOK, HAMMOND & KELL LTD.
(The London Map Centre)
22 Caxton Street,   **071-222 4945 (general)**
London SW1H OQU.   **071-222 2466 (O.S. sales)**

Subjects: Maps, guides.
Hours: Mon - Fri 9.00 - 5.00.
Services: Mail order, Ordnance Survey catalogues.

This is a two-level shop with over a million Ordnance Survey sheets stored with military precision in the basement, and general maps and town plans at ground level. Though concentrating largely on London and Britain, a range of foreign maps and guides is carried, and most normal enquiries can be dealt with — from travellers to Spain on charter flights to those weekending in Paris or taking an intercontinental journey. It never pays to be secretive when buying maps. By explaining why you want a certain map, the staff can quite often come up with a better one than you may have thought possible.

WESTMINSTER CATHEDRAL BOOKSHOP
Morpeth Terrace, London SW1P 1EP.   **071-828 5582**

Subjects: Catholic religion and theology.
Hours: Mon - Sat 10.00 - 5.30.
Services: Mail order, special orders.

The shop is approached down the steps beside the Conference Centre. The books cover all aspects of the Christian faith, mainly though not exclusively from a Roman Catholic viewpoint. There is a small children's section and records and cassettes are also stocked.

POPULAR BOOK CENTRE
87 Rochester Row, London SW1P 1LJ. **071-834 3534**

Subjects: General secondhand.
Hours: Mon - Sat 10.00 - 5.30.
Services: Exchange with half-price credit.

True to its title, popular books are stocked with the choice to exchange at half price, so plenty of reading at a very low price.

CATHOLIC TRUTH SOCIETY BOOKSHOP
25 Ashley Place, Westminster Cathedral Piazza,
London SW1P 1LT. **071-834 1363**

Subjects: Catholic religion and theology.
Hours: Mon - Fri 9.15 - 5.00. Sat 9.15 - 1.00.
Services: Special orders.

Popular books relevant to the Catholic faith, for adults and children, are sold here together with cards, rosaries and other religious requisites. However, the backbone of the stock is serious theology.

CHURCH HOUSE BOOKSHOP
31 Great Smith Street, London, SW1P 3BN. **071-222 5520**

Subjects: Theology, Christian spirituality, general.
Hours: Mon - Fri 9.00 - 5.00. Thu 9.00 - 6.00.
Services: Special orders, credit cards, mail order, new book bulletin.

This shop has a large range of Christian books, and also stocks some general titles, records and cassettes, posters and cards, and has a video hire library. Predominately Church of England in emphasis but not exclusively so.

WESTMINSTER ABBEY BOOKSHOP
20 Deans Yard, London SW1P 3PA.   **071-222 5565**

Subjects: General.
Hours: Mon - Sat 9.30 - 5.00.

This shop, set in the wall of Westminster Abbey, concentrates on things of interest for the visitor or tourist. It is quite spacious with half the room selling cards and souvenirs and the remainder stocking a general range of books including anything that has been written about the Abbey.

THE CHURCH LITERATURE ASSOCIATION
Faith House, 7 Tufton Street, London SW1P 3QN. 071-222 6952

Subjects: Theology, church history.
Hours: Mon - Fri 9.30 - 5.00.
Services: Credit cards, mail order, lists.

A most unusual-looking shop, it was designed by Lutyens more to resemble a church, with ornate ceilings, small balconies and a cross and it is a listed building. The books are well displayed in plenty of natural light and there is ample room to browse. As well as books they supply parishes with devotional articles, sheet music, etc.

MOTHERS UNION BOOKSHOP
Mary Sumner House,
24 Tufton Street, London SW1P 3RB.   **071-222 5533**

Subjects: Children's, Mothers' Union publications.
Hours: Mon - Fri 9.30 - 5.00.
Services: Credit cards, special orders.

This is a corner shop with an attractive wood panelled interior. The books are grouped by subject with an emphasis on family and Christianity. The ambience is relaxed and friendly.

TATE GALLERY SHOP
Millbank, London SW1P 4RY.   **071-834 5651**

Subjects: British and contemporary art.
Hours: Mon - Sat 10.00 - 5.30, Sun 2.00 - 5.30.
Services: Mail order, credit cards, catalogue of Tate Gallery publications.

Quite a large shop selling art books and postcards, prints and posters, with the more expensive items in glass cases. The books reflect the gallery's interest in British and foreign art since about 1850.

PAGES OF FUN
16 Terminus Place, London SW1V 1JR.   **071-834 7747**

Subjects: General.
Hours: Mon - Sat 9.00 a.m. - 10.00 p.m.

Paperback fiction, science fiction and horror are most prominent in this small shop opposite Victoria Station. Also pop music and general remainders and, on the back wall, a section of 'adult material'.

LONDON TOURIST BOARD BOOKSHOP
Tourist Information Centre,
Forecourt, Victoria Station, London SW1V 1JT.   **071-730 3488**

Subjects: Books on London and Great Britain, maps, guides.
Hours: Mon - Sat 9.00 - 7.00 (longer hours in Summer). Sun 9.00 - 4.30.
Services: Mail order (list), credit cards.

This shop is on a corner site at Victoria Station, a very strategic one for selling guide books to the capital and the country generally. Besides the more general guides there are books on walks, buildings, canals and bridges. Also in stock are posters, videos, slides, postcards and stamps. If the vagaries of British Rail timetables have caught you out there is no better place to kill time than here.

W.H. SMITH LTD.
Victoria Station   Eastern shop **071-828 2853**
London SW1V 1JT.   Western shop **071-834 2534**

Subjects: General, travel.
Hours: Eastern shop Mon - Sat 6.30 - 9.30. Sun 7.00 - 7.00.
                   Western shop Mon - Sat 6.30 - 10.00. Sun 8.00 - 9.00.
Services: Credit cards, special orders.

There are two WH Smiths at Victoria Station for the historic reason that two railway companies used the station until their amalgamation in 1923. Victoria East is by platforms 3 and 4 and has a good selection of continental maps and guides, whereas Victoria West is on what might be called the 'Brighton side' and is more the usual station mix of best sellers, leisure reading and magazines.

PADRE PIO BOOK SHOP CENTRE
10 Upper Tachbrook Street, London SW1V 1SH   071-834 5363

Subjects: Padre Pio, religious.
Hours: Mon - Sat 10.00 - 5.30.
Services: Special orders, mail order, list.

The society promoting the canonisation of Padre Pio (1887-1968), the stigmatised Capuchin monk of San Giovanni, runs this small religious bookshop and prayer centre in Victoria. Although only a few of Padre Pio's own writings have been translated into English there is an extensive literature about him, and this — together with relevant tapes and videos — is the shop's main stock. There are also some more general titles relating to the Catholic faith.

JOHN RANDALL
47 Moreton Street,   071-630 5331
London SW1V 2NY.   Fax 071-821 6544

Subjects: India, Central Asia, South East Asia.
Hours: Tue - Fri 10.00 - 6.00. Sat 10.00 - 5.00. (Often closed in August).
Services: Catalogues, mail order, credit cards.

A good stock of antiquarian, secondhand and new books covering all aspects of the above areas. They try to have available a wide range of books on Indian art, Balinese dancing, Tibetan exploration and Malayan magic. If you are looking for an Indonesian recipe, a history of Rangoon or information on the Silk Road they may well have the book for you.

J.A. ALLEN & CO. (THE HORSEMAN'S BOOKSHOP) LTD.
1 Lower Grosvenor Place,
Buckingham Palace Road,   071-828 8855
London SW1W OEL.   071-834 5606/7

Subjects: Horses.
Hours: Mon - Fri 9.00 - 5.30. Sat 9.00 - 1.00.
Services: Mail order, catalogue, credit cards, magazine subscriptions.

Appropriately located opposite the Royal Mews, this shop and publishing house stocks books on all aspects of the equine world, racing them, breeding them and caring for them. Principally new stock but they will obtain out of print and antiquarian books for their customers. They aim to keep every book current in Britain, and the major foreign ones, on horses. The bookshop is a Royal Warrant Holder by Appointment to H.M. The Queen and also to H.R.H. The Duke of Edinburgh.

W.H. SMITH LTD.
36 Sloane Square, London SW1W 8AP.   **071-730 0351**

Subjects: General.
Hours: Mon - Fri 9.00 - 6.30. Sat 9.00 - 6.00.
Services: Credit cards, special orders.

One of the best WHS shops in London situated in the lucrative catchment area of Sloane Square station, at the east end of the Kings Road, and serving the Chelsea set. The books are on the ground floor, generously displayed and the shop has a high turnover of best sellers.

PETER JONES
Sloane Square, London SW1W 8EL.   **071-730 3434**

Subjects: Children's.
Hours: Mon - Fri 9.00 - 5.30, Wed 9.30 - 7.00, Sat 9.00 - 5.30.

On the third floor of this department store is a small adjunct to the toy department, selling children's books with educational books well represented.

THE WELL
2 Eccleston Place, London SW1W 9NE.   **071-730 7303**

Subjects: Christian books.
Hours: Mon - Sat 9.30 - 6.00.
Services: Coffee bar, special orders.

Opposite Victoria Coach Station in Elizabeth Street is the Well Bookshop at the side of a large coffee bar, which must be a pleasing sight to travellers, who are welcome and can browse among the Christian books, videos and music cassettes. Children's stories, Bibles and prayer books are available as the shop is in association with St. Michael's Church, Chester Square.

HATCHARDS AT HARVEY NICHOLS
Knightsbridge, London SW1X 7RJ.   **071-235 5000 Extn. 2171**

Subjects: General.
Hours: Mon - Fri 10.00 - 7.00. Sat 10.00 - 6.00.
Services: Credit cards, mail order, catalogue, free delivery Inner London.

This offshoot of the excellent Hatchards is on the fourth floor of Harvey Nichols and carries on a smaller scale much of the same quality books in the general range as the parent shop. The books are attractively displayed on tables or shelved under clear subject headings.

HARRODS
Knightsbridge, London SW1X 7XL.   **071-730 1234**

Subjects: General, art, paperbacks, children's.
Hours: Mon - Sat 9.00 - 6.00. Wed 9.30 - 7.00.
Services: Mail order, signed copies list, credit cards.

There are three large book sections on the second floor, one for paperbacks, one general books and the third for arts-related books. In addition there is a separate children's book department on the fourth floor. All of the books are well displayed, with many 'face out' on traditional wooden shelving. There is a comprehensive range of categories including travel, computers and cookery. The adjoining arts room contains books on art, antiques, architecture, interior design, cinema, photography, poetry, plays, music and fine leather bindings.

Signed copies are a major feature of the department, with many formal signing sessions. A list of customers interested in signings and signed copies is maintained.

PSYCHIC NEWS BOOKSHOP
The Spiritualist Association of Great Britain
33 Belgrave Square, London SW1X 8QL.   **071-235 3351**

Subjects: Spiritualism.
Hours: Mon - Fri 10.00 - 7.00. Sat 10.00 - 4.30. Sun 3.00 - 8.00.

This is a small shop in the foyer of the Association selling books, pamphlets and journals on their subject. They are rather precise about the psychic world and do not have books from the wilder shores of occult and magic.

BOOKS ON SPORT (PIPELINE)
Ground Floor, Lillywhites Ltd.,
Piccadilly Circus, London SW1Y 4QF.   **071-930 3181**

Subjects: Sport.
Hours: Mon - Sat 9.30 - 6.00. Thu 9.30 - 7.00.
Services: Special orders, mail order.

An ideal spot to have a selection of books on sport, with room to browse. Their sports books cover a wide range including cricket, tennis, squash, rugby, football, golf, bowling, croquet, snooker, skiing, sailing, windsurfing, climbing, walking, cycling, riding, fishing, martial arts and health and fitness. In the appropriate season they have one of the best selections of skiing books on offer in London. Calendars and videos on sport are also stocked.

DESIGN CENTRE BOOKSHOP   071-839 8000
28 Haymarket,   **Extn. 4218 or 4219**
London SW1Y 4SU.   **Fax 071-925 2130**

Subjects: Design.
Hours: Mon, Tue 10.00 - 6.00. Wed - Sat 10.00 - 8.00. Sun 1.00 - 6.00.
Services: Mail order, lists, credit cards.

The bookshop is at the rear of the Design Centre, up some stairs. Among the clearly marked sections are design (in all its aspects), graphics, architecture, engineering, crafts, fashion and photography, and of course they stock their own Design Council publications. There is also an extensive magazine section. The whole shop is well worth a visit for the constantly changing ranges of interesting items exhibited.

KIWI FRUITS NEW ZEALAND BOOKSHOP
6 Royal Opera Arcade, London SW1Y 4UY.   **071-930 4587**

Subjects: New Zealand publications, travel.
Hours: Mon - Fri 9.00 - 5.30. Sat 10.00 - 4.00.
Services: Mail order, agent for New Zealand Government printers, window of small ads. mostly accommodation and jobs.

This shop is in the arcade between The Haymarket and Lower Regent Street. It is small inside but stocks over a thousand titles from or about New Zealand. It has a good range of travel books not unsurprisingly, as Kiwis counter the peripheral with the peripatetic. Craft items, jewellery and postcards are also sold.

INSTITUTE OF CONTEMPORARY ARTS BOOKSHOP
The Nash House,
12 Carlton House Terrace, London SW1Y 5AH.   **071-930 0493**

Subjects: The Arts, general, feminism.
Hours: Mon - Sun 12.00 - 9.00.

The I.C.A. is towards the Trafalgar Square end of the Mall. The shop is a small part of a complex of galleries, cinemas, theatres, etc. and is located to the side of the main entrance. There are books on photography, psychology, philosophy, politics, films and a good selection of modern fiction, also an unusual range of artists' postcards. It is a very British solution to 'the modern' to house it in Regency grandeur.

THE PLANNING BOOKSHOP
Town and Country Planning Association,
17 Carlton House Terrace, London SW1Y 5AS.   **071-930 8903**

Subjects: Environmental studies, transportation, energy, housing.
Hours: Mon - Fri 9.30 - 5.30.
Services: Catalogue, mail order, suppliers to institutions.

You enter this building from Carlton House Terrace which backs on to the Mall and walk up a grand staircase or take a lift to the first floor where the shop occupies one room. The Association is a voluntary body founded in 1899, whose aim is to revitalise Britain's regions and fight urban decay, and the books it stocks are towards this end.

PICKERING AND CHATTO
Incorporating Dawsons of Pall Mall,   **071-930 2515**
16/17 Pall Mall, London SW1Y 5NB.   **Fax 071-930 8627**

Subjects: Antiquarian specialising in English literature, economics, science, medicine, manuscripts and autographs; scholarly editions in the history of ideas (publishers of).
Hours: Mon - Fri 9.30 - 5.30.
Services: Mail order, catalogue and lists, library and institutional supply.

One rings a bell to enter this deep carpeted shop in Pall Mall which has been Pickering and Chatto's premises since 1981. The interior is as sumptuous as the address is prestigious with books impressively marshalled in old cabinets and cases. The stock is entirely antiquarian, the service expert and helpful, but it is not really a place for the uninitiated.

FARLOWS OF PALL MALL
5 Pall Mall, London SW1Y 5NP.   **071-839 2423**

Subjects: Shooting and fishing.
Hours: Mon - Fri 9.00 - 6.00. Sat 9.00 - 4.00.
Services: Credit cards, special orders.

The shop at the Trafalgar Square end of Pall Mall is principally a tackle shop but they do have technical books, monographs and directories as well as books on how to cook the victims who find themselves at the wrong end of their excellent equipment.

ST GEORGE'S GALLERY BOOKS LTD.
8 Duke Street, St. James', London SW1Y 6BN.   **071-930 0935**

Subjects: Fine and decorative arts, architecture.
Hours: Mon - Fri 10.00 - 6.00.
Services: Mail order, catalogues from recent exhibitions.

Four rows of books in the window give a good representation of the stock inside, which covers the whole range of the pictorial and decorative arts. Despite appearances inside, with people working at desks, etc., it is a shop with a basement and upper floor crammed with books and monographs. In its field of specialisation it is most comprehensive.

THOMAS HENEAGE ART BOOKS
42 Duke Street, St. James's,   **071-720 1503**
London SW1Y 6DJ.   **Fax 071-720 3158**

Subjects: Fine, decorative and ancient art.
Hours: Mon - Fri 10.00 - 6.00. Sat 10.00 - 2.00.
Services: Mail order, library supply, foreign book orders, postage
             world wide.

This elegant shop in the heart of the St. James's art gallery district, holds an enormous stock of artists' monographs and catalogues raisonnés from the old masters to the contemporary. Ancient art, sculpture, furniture, porcelain, silver, jewellery and antiques are also subjects covered. Generally the principal reference works on art in any language whether new or out-of-print are held.

SIMS REED LTD.   **071-493 5660**
58 Jermyn Street, London SW1Y 6LX.   **Fax 071-493 8468**

Subjects: Modern illustrated, antiquarian, out-of-print art books.
Hours: Mon - Fri 10.00 - 6.00.
Services: Mail order, catalogues.

An inviting shop selling rare and antiquarian books, specialising in modern illustrated books and the fine arts. The books are arranged by nationality but it would be best to locate something by asking the friendly assistant, as the sense of order seems personal. Book lists are produced monthly and mail order accounts for most of their business.

SPINK & SON LTD.
5/7 King Street, London SW1Y 6QS.   **071-930 7888**

Subjects: Books on coins and medals, new and secondhand.
Hours: Mon - Fri 9.30 - 5.30.
Services: Mail order, special orders, catalogue.

Numismatists will probably know this second floor book room where new, secondhand and antiquarian books on coin and medal collections are sold. Much of Spink's business is mail order but browsers are welcomed.

HERALDRY TODAY
10 Beauchamp Place, London SW3 1NQ.   **071-584 1656**

Subjects: Heraldry, genealogy, topography.
Hours: Mon, Tue, Wed 9.30 - 5.00.
Services: Mail order, catalogue, library and institution supply,
                search service.

Up and down a few stairs, through a courtyard, one finds the two
rooms where the books are. Most of the trade is mail order, in one
room are new books and in the other antiquarian and secondhand
ones.

THE MAP HOUSE
54 Beauchamp Place, London SW3 1NY.   **071-589 4325/9821**

Subjects: Antiquarian maps and prints.
Hours: Mon - Fri 9.45 - 5.45, Sat 10.30 - 5.00.
Services: Credit cards, special orders.

A very large collection of antique maps of the United Kingdom and
of the rest of the world; also antique atlases, engravings and globes.
There are a few modern books for sale on the collecting of these
items.

JOHN SANDOE (BOOKS) LTD.
10 Blacklands Terrace, London SW3 2SP.   **071-589 9473**

Subjects: General.
Hours: Mon - Sat 9.30 - 5.30.
Services: Mail order, catalogue at Christmas.

In this shop, which has been here since 1955, the most has certainly
been made of a little. It is on three levels, overflowing with books
in every corner. On the first floor are the paperbacks, well displayed
and various, in the basement is a small room for children's books,
and at ground level the general stock with new titles on window
ledges and tables. Technical and academic books are not stocked,
but the shop is a cornucopia of good things rather randomly
arranged though helpful assistance is readily to hand.

NATIONAL ARMY MUSEUM BOOKSHOP
Royal Hospital Road, London SW3 4HT.　　　　**071-730 0717**

Subjects:　British and Indian armies.
Hours:　　Mon - Sat 10.00 - 5.00. Sun 2.00 - 5.00.
Services:　Book list, mail order.

A small room inside this Army Museum stocks books on the British and Indian armies including biographies, regimental and campaign histories, and books on badges, medals and uniforms. They have a children's section and although not a large stock, it must be very convenient for visitors interested in the battles of the past to be able to further their knowledge by buying books before they leave.

TROCCHI RARE BOOKS LTD.
Antiquarius, Stands L8-L9,
15 Flood Street, King's Road,　　　　　**071-351 3820**
London SW3 4PW.　　　　　　　**071-624 1214 (home)**

Subjects:　General antiquarian and collectors' books.
Hours:　　Mon - Sat 10.00 - 6.00.
Services:　Books bought, credit cards.

This stall in the antique market carries some 2,300 volumes of collectables without speciality of subject.

BARBARA STONE
Antiquarius,
135 King's Road, London SW3 4PW.　　　**071-351 0963**

Subjects:　Rare books; illustrated, children's, private press.
Hours:　　Mon - Sat 10.30 - 5.30.
Services:　Books bought, catalogues (four per annum), wants lists.

Rare books with specialisation in nineteenth and twentieth century illustrated books, children's books from the eighteenth through to the twentieth century and private presses.

DON KELLY BOOKS
Antiquarius, Stand M13
135 King's Road, London SW3 4PW.   **071-352 4690**

Subjects: Fine and applied art, new and secondhand.
Hours: Mon - Sat 10.00 - 6.00.
Services: Catalogue (annually), search service, credit cards.

Two small stalls in the antique market house about a thousand books on painting, the decorative arts and collectables.

A.F. ROE & D.L. MOORE
Chenil Galleries, Stands D3-D4,
181-183 King's Road, London SW3 5EB.   **071-376 4706**

Subjects: Modern rare books.
Hours: Mon - Sat 10.30 - 5.30.
Services: Catalogues (three per annum).

This stall houses a select stock of rare books, concentrating on the fine arts from 1880-1980. This includes monographs, illustrated books, artists' letters and drawings in books, and an extensive stock of rare exhibition catalogues. There is also a small selection of children's classics and antiquarian books.

WILLCOCKS ANTIQUES
Chenil Galleries, Stand G3,
181-183 King's Road, London SW3 5EB.   **071 352 7384**

Subjects: Illustrated and children's books.
Hours: Mon - Sat 11.00 - 6.00.
Services: Books bought.

An antiques stall selling illustrated and children's books, mainly circa 1850-1930, as well as prints, fans and costume jewellery.

IL LIBRO
Chenil Galleries, Stands C8-C9,
181-183 Kings Road, London SW3 5EB.   **071-352 9041**

Subjects: Antiquarian, natural history.
Hours: Mon - Sat 10.00 - 6.00.
Services: Books bought, book binding.

Quite a large stall in the antique market specialising in ornithological and botanical books and natural history generally, fine bindings, illustrated books, and with some antiquarian books in French. Also some general stock. Prices range from £5 to £20,000.

JOANNA BOOTH
247 Kings Road, London SW3 5EL.   **071-352 8998**

Subjects: French antiquarian books.
Hours: Mon - Sat 10.00 - 6.00.
Services: Mail order, catalogue.

An intriguing melange of things to buy here as well as old French books, there are carvings, tapestries, textiles and old master drawings. Pleasantly informal with more of the appearance of a private house than a shop.

HARRINGTON BROS.
The Chelsea Antique Market,   **071-352 5689**
253 Kings Road, London SW3 5EL.   **Fax 071 -823 3449**

Subjects: General, antiquarian, plate books, bound sets, travel, natural history.
Hours: Mon - Sat 10.00 - 6.00.
Services: Mail order, occasional lists, books bought.

The window of this small antique market is filled with antiquarian books and inside at street level is a small stall displaying an introductory stock. Anyone showing genuine interest will be taken up a narrow staircase to two rooms with many books, colour plates and bound sets; a reward for the curious.

CHELSEA RARE BOOKS
313 Kings Road, London SW3 5EP.   **071-351 0950**

Subjects: First editions, rare books, secondhand.
Hours: Mon - Sat 10.00 - 6.00.
Services: Mail order, catalogue.

An interesting shop for the collector or browser. Most books openly displayed with the rarer items in cabinets. At ground level the emphasis is on 18th and 19th Century English literature with tables and chairs provided for customers to examine the books. Downstairs are prints, maps, watercolours, and books on art and architecture.

PENGUIN ARTS BOOKSHOP
157 Kings Road, London SW3 5TX.   **071-351 1915**

Subjects: Arts.
Hours: Mon - Sat 9.30 a.m. - 11.00 p.m.
Services: Post-a-book, credit cards.

This shop has recently been rearranged to create more internal space and more attractive displays of all merchandise. It now specialises in an exciting range of books on the arts. There is also a broad range of fine art cards, postcards, posters, wrapping paper and talking tapes.

GREY HOUSE BOOKS
12a Lawrence Street, Chelsea, London SW3.   **071-352 7725**

Subjects: True crime, detective fiction, Sherlockiana.
Hours: Seven days per week, no set times.
Services: Regular catalogues on all three subjects.

Grey House Books is not the most conventional of bookshops. It is a little grey house in a picturesque and peaceful part of London near the River Thames but only one and a half miles from Harrods. If you are seeking books on true crime (a large and comprehensive range including notable British trials), detective fiction (mostly first editions in hardback) or Sherlockiana/Conan Doyle (over three hundred items in stock) then this is where to go. Children are welcome; there are three cats to amuse them while you browse in peace. Open seven days a week including Bank Holidays, with no set hours, but please telephone first for an appointment.

TETRIC BOOKSHOP
116 Clapham High Street, London SW4 7UH.   **071-622 5344**

Subjects: General.
Hours: Mon - Fri 10.00 - 6.00. Sat 10.00 - 5.30.
Services: Special orders, local events board.

A good small general bookshop very much in tune with its local community. Mostly paperbacks with the contemporary concerns of politics, feminism and sociology well represented.

ORBIS BOOKS (LONDON) LTD.
66 Kenway Road,   **071-370 2210**
London SW5 0RD.   **Fax 071-602 5541**

Subjects: Soviet and East European studies.
Hours: Mon - Fri 9.30 - 5.30, Sat 9.30 - 4.30.
Services: Credit cards, mail order, catalogue, library and university supply.

Stocks books in English on all aspects of East European and Soviet affairs together with books in Polish, Russian, Czech and Ukrainian. They also carry a selection of Polish records, music cassettes and videos of Polish films.

THE ATOZ BOOK CENTRE
11 Kenway Road (off Earl's Court Road),
London SW5 0RP.   **071-370 0236**

Subjects: Martial arts.
Hours: Mon - Sat 10.00 - 6.00.
Services: Mail order, all major credit cards over the telephone.

This small shop, now in Earl's Court, has all the books a fighting monk may require from Kendo to Kung Fu. The associated equipment is also sold.

W.H. SMITH LTD.
266 Earl's Court Road, London SW5 9AS.   **071-370 3201**

Subjects: General.
Hours: Mon - Sat 9.00 - 7.00.
Services: Credit cards, special orders.

A large one-floored branch of Smith's with plenty of table display room for their hard backed and new titles. Educational books and maps and guides are well represented.

POETRY SOCIETY BOOKSHOP
21 Earl's Court Square, London SW5 9DE.   **071-373 7861/2**

Subjects: Poetry.
Hours: Mon - Fri 10.00 - 5.00 (event evenings until 7.30).
Services: Mail order, occasional lists.

This is a large, ground floor room crammed with slim volumes of verse, mostly contemporary. The stock covers English language poetry (including North America and the Third World) and poetry in translation. The Poetry Society also publishes its own magazine, *Poetry Review.*

RESPONSE COMMUNITY BOOKSHOP
**300 Old Brompton Road, Earl's Court,
London SW5 9JE.**   **071-370 4606**

Subjects: General secondhand.
Hours: Mon - Sat 11.00 - 7.00.
Services: Books bought.

A general secondhand bookshop with a self-service coffee bar at the back of the shop.

BOOKSTOP
**36 Vanston Place, Fulham,
London SW6 1AX.**   **071-381 8764**

Subjects: General.
Hours: Mon - Sat 9.30 - 6.00.
Services: Special orders, credit cards.

Predominantly paperback books line this general bookshop which has a good selection of fiction and other subjects, all clearly marked including a children's section. A bright, modern shop, just off the North End Road should prove a welcome addition to this area.

WEST LONDON BOOKS LTD.
15 Jerdan Place, London SW6 1BE.   **071-385 8334**

Subjects: Remainders, general subjects, art and design.
Hours: Mon - Sat 10.30 - 5.30.
Services: Credit cards.

There are some full-price books, hardback and paperback, but remainders are their main concern — arranged under subject with sections marked clearly (antiques, cookery, etc.). At any time there are over 1,500 half-price titles in stock. Plenty of bargains here for adults and children.

W.H. SMITH LTD.
320 North End Road, Fulham, London SW6 1NG. 071-385 9585

Subjects: General.
Hours: Mon - Sat 9.00 - 6.00. Tue 9.30 - 6.00.
Services: Special orders, credit cards.

The books are on the right on entering, past the newspapers and magazines. There is a range of general non-fiction subjects and a good paperback fiction section with some contemporary fiction. Bestsellers are stocked in paperback and hardback.

JOHN THORNTON
634 King's Road, London SW6 2DU.   **071-736 6181**

Subjects: General, secondhand and antiquarian, theology.
Hours: Mon - Sat 10.00 - 5.30.
Services: Books bought, mail order.

A long narrow shop, like a gallery, with secondhand and antiquarian books on general subjects, but in particular theology, which accounts for about one third of their 10,000 or so volumes. A reserve stock of theological books is kept in premises across the courtyard at the back, and can be viewed on request.

BOOKS FOR CHILDREN
97 Wandsworth Bridge Road, London SW6 2TD.   071-384 1821

Subjects: Children's books (0-16 years).
Hours: Mon 10.00 - 6.00. Tue - Sat 9.30 - 6.00.
Services: Special orders (including books for adults), school suppliers.

The experienced and friendly staff are here to help the children choose from their wide range of books and cassettes. The stock ranges from cloth books through to teenage fiction and non-fiction. They also stock educational books. Browsers of all ages are most welcome.

HAN-SHAN TANG LTD.
717 Fulham Road,
London SW6 5UL.   **071-731 2447**

Subjects: China, Japan, Korea.
Hours: Mon - Fri 10.00 - 6.00 by appointment only.
Services: International mail order, catalogue, institutional supply.

It is necessary to ring the bell in order to enter this bookshop which specialises in China, Japan and Korea. Upon entering you will be directed to the section of your particular interest and allowed to browse with the knowledge that there is a back up to the books on show with a basement stock. Mail order is the main concern here and they claim to have one of the largest stocks of books on the arts and cultures of their specialist areas. Scholarly books are listed in their catalogue but interested customers are very welcome to browse and see the books in person.

THE CONSTANT READER BOOKSHOP
627 Fulham Road, London SW6 5UQ.   **071-731 0218**

Subjects: General, secondhand, oriental.
Hours: Mon - Sat 10.30 - 6.30.
Services: Books bought, mail order.

An excellent secondhand bookshop covering a wide range of subjects
both hard and soft backed. They are strong on illustrated books, the arts, military history and especially books on travelling in the Orient.

BENEDICTS BOOKSHOP
92 Lillie Road, London SW6 7SR.   **071-385 4426**

Subjects: Language teaching, general new and secondhand.
Hours: Mon - Fri 9.30 - 6.00. Sat 10.00 - 4.00.
Services: School and library supply, mail order, special orders.

This bookshop specialises in language teaching materials with books in English and foreign languages and audio, video, tapes, cassettes, film, etc. to assist foreigners with English and the English with foreign languages. They are also enlarging their general stock to provide books in this area, both new and secondhand, but maintianing their large specialist stock as their main function.

THE RUSSIAN ORTHODOX CATHEDRAL BOOKSHOP
Cathedral of the Assumption and All Saints,
67 Ennismore Gardens, London SW7 1NH.   **071-376 7071**

Subjects: Orthodox Christianity (all aspects).
Hours: Mon - Fri only by appointment by telephone. Sat 4.30 - 5.30, 7.30 - 8.00. Sun 9.30 - 10.30, 12.00 - 1.00.
Services: Mail order, catalogue.

This bookshop within the Cathedral is in principle open seven days a week, but on weekdays you will need to telephone first. The stock must be unique in London in its coverage of Orthodox Christianity. Most of the books are in English and cover Orthodox and pre-schism theology, liturgy, spiritual life, biography and art.

IMPERIAL COLLEGE UNION BOOKSTORE
223 Sherfield Building,
Imperial College, London SW7 2AZ.   **071-589 5218**

Subjects: Engineering, science.
Hours: Mon - Fri 9.00 - 6.00.
Services: Special orders, mail order, lists.

Although this shop is open to the public it is rather difficult to find at the centre of Imperial College. It carries an impressive stock on all branches of engineering, the physical and life sciences, mathematics, management and the history of science and technology, and also keeps German language books for the nearby Goethe Institute. There is also lighter reading, cards, stationery, drawing equipment and general merchandise.

DILLONS AT THE SCIENCE MUSEUM
Exhibition Road, London SW7 2DD.   **071-938 8255**

Subjects: Science, technology.
Hours: Mon - Sat 10.00 - 6.00. Sun 11.00 - 6.00.
Services: Mail order, educational supply, credit cards.

Catering specifically for the sciences and reflecting the permanent exhibitions within the museum, Dillons at the Science Museum specialises in current and historical science and technology (including transport, astronomy, horology, nutrition, photography, industrial archaeology etc.). There is also an extensive children's section with an emphasis on experiments and activities. All the Science Museum's own publications are kept as well as books for the general visitor to the museum and text books for the scholarly reader. The shop has a separate street entrance and only if visitors wish to enter the museum do they have to pay admission.

GEOLOGICAL MUSEUM BOOKSHOP
Exhibition Road, London SW7 2DE.   **071-938 9126**

Subjects: Geology, minerology, geological maps.
Hours: Mon - Sat 10.00 - 6.00, Sun 1.00 - 6.00.
Services: Mail order, gift and book catalogue.

Newly enlarged and refurbished, the Geological Museum shop is an excellent place for all things geological and mineralogical. The new layout allows customers to view the wide range of merchandise at leisure. Minerals, compasses, geological hard hats and hammers, cards, wall charts, posters and gifts are also stocked.

OPPENHEIM & CO. LTD.
7/9 Exhibition Road, London SW7 2HE.   **071-584 5641**

Subjects: Art, photography, design, children's, general and
Hours: transport.
Services: Mon - Sat 8.30 - 6.30. Sun various.
               Credit cards, special orders, library supply.

Sunday opening hours at this bookshop, a short walk from the Science Museum, will be welcome especially as there is a specialist transport department upstairs. The ground floor is divided into a constantly changing stock of remainders and reduced review copies whereas upstairs, new and out of print books on motoring, aviation, ships, aircraft and modelling have a separat room. Ninety per cent of all stock is at reduced prices.

F. PULTENEY & CO. (BOOKS) LTD.
22 Thurloe Street, London SW7 2LT.   **071-589 0522**

Subjects: Art, general, remainders.
Hours: Mon - Fri 9.30 - 5.30, Sat 11.00 - 3.00.
Services: Library supply.

A one-roomed shop at street level with stalls lined and tables piled with books. The window displays their bargain books, clearly priced. The stock is of good quality.

THE MEDICI GALLERY
26 Thurloe Street, London SW7 2LT.   **071-589 1363**

Subjects: Art.
Hours: Mon - Fri 9.00 - 5.30, Sat 9.00 - 5.00.
Services: Exhibitions, framing.

A shop selling artists materials and small book section of art books and Medici publications.

VICTORIA & ALBERT MUSEUM BOOKSHOP
Cromwell Road, London SW7 2RL.   **071-938 8434**

Subjects: Arts, crafts, antiques, textiles.
Hours: Mon - Sat 10.00 - 5.30, Sun 2.30 - 5.30.
Services: Mail order, catalogue.

One of the more spacious museum bookshops, with many sections all devoted to the study, preservation and restoration of beautiful artifacts.

ZAMANA GALLERY BOOKSHOP
Ismaili Centre, Opp. the V. & A. Museum,   **071-584 6612/3**
1 Cromwell Gardens, London SW7 2SL   **Extn. 46**

Subjects: Islamic and Third World art, architecture and textiles.
Hours: Tue - Sat 10.00 - 5.30. Sun 12.00 - 5.30. Mon closed.
Services: Special orders, mail order, credit cards.

The Ismaili Centre is the large new building opposite the V. & A. and houses the Zamana Gallery which exhibits the art, architecture and textiles of Islamic and Third World countries. The bookshop within the foyer covers the same subjects in its well-displayed stock and also sells relevant cassettes, records, postcards and posters.

JOHN MENZIES (GB) LTD.
50/52 Old Brompton Road, London SW7 3DX.　　　**071-589 3769**

Subjects: General.
Hours: Mon - Fri 7.00 - 8.00. Sat, Sun 8.00 - 6.00.
Services: Credit cards.

A combination of stationery and books sold, which is the usual mix with Menzies. A generous paperback section, mostly fiction, arranged alphabetically by author and central tables with bargain hardbacks.

LA PAGE BOOKSHOP
7 Harrington Road,
South Kensington, London SW7 3ES.　　　**071-589 5991**

Subjects: French books, *bandes dessinées.*
Hours: Mon - Fri 8.15 - 6.15, Sat 10.00 - 5.00.
Services: Subscription to French magazines, monthly lists, credit cards.

It has the appearance at the front of a small stationers, but through the narrow shop and down a few stairs is a room full of French books with a French speaking assistant to help. It is now the major specialist in *bandes dessinées,* carrying about 1,500 titles. There are guides and maps to France and some cassettes. The French stationery section will be appreciated by those who prefer writing on squared rather than on lined paper.

KENSINGTON MUSIC SHOP
9 Harrington Road, London SW7 3ES.　　　**071-589 9054**

Subjects: Music.
Hours: Mon - Fri 9.00 - 5.45, Sat 9.00 - 4.00.
Services: Credit cards, international mail order, concert information.

This is a shop of international repute and numbers many major musicians among its customers. It is in the group which includes Chimes and the Barbican Music Shop and like the others is staffed by trained musicians. Musical biographies, sheet music, instruction books for musical instruments; musical instruments and accessories are all sold here. There is a notice board displaying information about concerts and advertising music lessons and musical instruments for sale.

THE FRENCH BOOKSHOP
28 Bute Street, London SW7 3EX.   **071-584 2840**

Subjects: French books.
Hours: Mon - Fri 10.00 - 6.00 (8.30 - 6.00 in term time). Sat 10.00 - 5.30.
Services: Special orders.

A bright blue painted shop with striped blue and white awning, spacious and friendly inside. They carry a whole range of French books, including the best-sellers, art and cookery books, and *bandes dessinées*. There are cartoons by Claire Bretecher and others on sale. The bilingual owner can offer specialist advice on her extensive range of books and takes pride in her children's section. Students from the Lycee nearby are well served. Maps and guides of France, especially Paris, are stocked here. There are also some video cassettes, books on cassette and games such as monopoly — all in French.

WATERSTONE'S BOOKSELLERS
99-101 Old Brompton Road, London SW7 3LE.   **071-581 8522**

Subjects: General.
Hours: Mon - Fri 9.30 - 9.00 . Sat 9.30 - 7.00. Sun 12.00 - 6.00.
Services: Special orders, mail order, school and library supply, out of print book search, credit cards.

Recently enlarged, this was the first branch of Waterstone's. They have a corner site, now with three floors, all devoted to an excellent stock in general subjects. In particular, fiction, art, biography, cookery and gardening are well represented. The staff in all departments are knowledgeable and maintain the stock themselves.

GLOUCESTER ROAD BOOKSHOP
123 Gloucester Road, London SW7 4TE.　　　　**071-370 3503**

Subjects: General secondhand and modern first editions.
Hours: Mon - Fri 8.30 - 10.30. Sat & Sun 10.30 - 6.30.
Services: Credit cards, books bought, catalogues, mail order, search services.

Three or four minutes' walk south of the Gloucester Road tube station, this deservedly popular shop caters to an educated reading public as well as having something for the collector.

It is particularly good on literature, biography, history, travel and children's books — and there is a small French section. Prints and ephemera are also sold.

H. KARNAC (BOOKS) LTD.
56/58 Gloucester Road,　　　　**071-584 3303**
London SW7 4QY.　　　　**071-823 7743**

Subjects: General, psychoanalysis, psychotherapy, analytical, psychology.
Hours: Mon - Sat 9.00 - 6.00.
Services: Mail order, catalogue, subscriptions to journals, library and institutional supply.

A general stock of hardback and paperback titles and a vast range of books on their specialisations; arguably the widest selection in the country.

NATURAL HISTORY MUSEUM BOOKSHOP
Cromwell Road,　　　　**071-938 9285**
London SW7 5BD.　　　　**Fax 071-938 8880**

Subjects: Natural history.
Hours: Mon - Sat 10.00 - 5.40. Sun 2.00 - 5.40.
Services: Mail order, catalogues.

Every aspect of natural history is represented here at every level of appreciation, children's books rubbing shoulders with the driest technical monographs. As well as other publishers' books they carry the whole range of BM(NH) publications. The shop is just inside the main entrance and has recently been totally refurbished, with an extra floor added.

PARKS
c/o South Bank Polytechnic,
220 Wandsworth Road, London SW8 2JZ.
071-928 8989
Ext. 3268

Subjects: Building, planning, architecture.
Hours: Mon - Fri 9.30 - 2.00. 3.00 - 6.00 (termtime only).
Services: Special orders, mail order.

JOHN BUCKLE BOOKSHOP
170 Wandsworth Road, London SW8 2LA.
071-627 0599

Subjects: Marxist-Leninist.
Hours: Mon - Sat 12.00 - 6.00.
Services: Special orders, mail order, catalogue.

The works of Marx, Engels, Lenin, Stalin and comrade Enver Hoxha are stocked here along with other revolutionary literature and Marxist-Leninist newspapers from throughout the world. Books from Albania are a speciality. The shop shares premises with the Workers' Publications Centre who represent the mail order side of the business.

NEW UJAMAA LTD.
14 Brixton Road,
London SW9 6BU.
071-820 1855
Fax 071-820 1855

Subjects: Multi-cultural.
Hours: Mon - Fri 10.00 - 6.30. Sat 10.30 - 5.00.
Services: Special orders to teachers and schools, mail order catalogue.

New Ujamaa Ltd. is a co-operative which aims to stimulate interest in the culture of developing countries. Hand-made crafts from Third World countries are stocked, the emphasis being on fair trade.
Books are concentrated on the Third World countries, racism and international women's issues. There is also literature by African, Caribbean and Latin American writers, and health, cookery and children's sections.

INDEX BOOKCENTRE (INDEXREACH LTD.)
10-12 Atlantic Road, Brixton, London SW9 8HY.   071-274 8342

Subjects: General, educational.
Hours: Mon - Sat 10.00 - 6.00.
Services: Special orders, institutional supply, supply for events and exhibitions.

A well lit, plate glass fronted shop, which is unusual in this area of Brixton, stocking a very good general selection of books with African and Caribbean sections for the local Black community, also women's writing. There is a children's corner and other subjects are well defined with strong politics and history sections. They also have a good educational section as they supply schools and colleges — a very good, well stocked bookshop.

THE ACME COMIC SHOP
391 Coldharbour Lane, Brixton, London SW9 8LQ. 071-274 6697

Subjects: Comics and graphic novels.
Hours: Mon - Sat 10.00 - 6.00.
Services: Credit cards.

This shop specialises in comics and stocks titles from the United Kingdom, the United States, Europe and Japan. There is an extensive range of new publications and back issues and an exceptionally wide range of independent comics and graphic novels.

CHELSEA GALLERY (IL LIBRO)
The Plaza, G5, 535 King's Road,
London SW10 0TZ.   **071-823 3248**

Subjects: Antiquarian, fine bindings, botany, ornithology.
Hours: Mon 2.00 - 7.00. Tue - Sat 10.00 - 7.00.
Services: Search service, credit cards.

Recently opened, this spacious and well-decorated shop in the new Plaza development has books lining one long wall, and prints on the wall opposite and on a central table. There is a good range of subjects with some specialisation in botany and ornithology. These are books for the collector with prices ranging from £30 to £20,000. There are some fine decorative prints from the sixteenth through to the nineteenth century and a collection of old maps. The owner with his cultivated taste and cosmopolitan interests, makes a visit here a very great pleasure.

PAN BOOKSHOP
158 Fulham Road, London SW10 9PR.   **071-373 4997**

Subjects: General.
Hours: Mon - Sat 10.00 - 10.00. Sun 1.00 - 9.30.
Services: Special orders for any book in print, mail order, credit cards.

This is a fairly large general bookshop with a good mix of hardbacks and paperbacks in all areas and a large back stock of books for which there is a continual demand. It is well lit and the stock is clearly displayed under subject headings. Strong on fiction in both hardback and paperback, with travel (narrative and guides), art and interior design, reference, religion and philosophy well represented and an imaginatively stocked children's section. Signed copies of new books are a special feature. The staff are helpful, friendly and knowledgeable.

MARTIN THE NEWSAGENT
66-68 St. Johns Road,
Clapham Junction, London SW11 1PT.　　　　　**071-223 9415**

Subjects:　General.
Hours:　　Mon - Sat 7.30 - 6.00. Sun 8.00 - 1.00.
Services:　Special orders, credit cards.

One corner of Martin's is made over to books in this branch with a paperback stand down the centre selling the usual popular titles. Atlases, maps and dictionaries are stocked with a smattering of titles in most subjects.

BOOKSTOP
75 St. John's Road, Clapham Junction,
London SW11 1QY.　　　　　　　　**071-978 5208**

Subjects:　General.
Hours:　　Mon - Fri 9.30 - 6.30. Sat 9.30 - 6.00.
Services　Special orders, credit cards.

A general bookshop with a good mix of paperbacks and hardbacks in fiction and other subjects, all clearly marked, and including a children's section. It is a bright modern shop in the main street about four hundred yards from Clapham Junction railway station.

AVALON COMICS AND BOOKS
143 Lavender Hill, London SW11 5RA.　　　**071-924 3609**

Subjects:　Comics, new and secondhand, graphic novels.
Hours:　　Mon - Fri 11.00 - 5.45. Sat 9.00 - 5.45.
Services:　Mail order, wants list, standing orders on comic imports,
　　　　　　credit cards.

This shop specialises in American comics for adults and children, including large numbers of back issues and some collectors' items. Imports are flown in weekly from the United States and Canada. Graphic novels, compilations of comics, Catalan publications, cartoon books and some secondhand science fiction, horror books and comic-related material are also stocked. The service is friendly and efficient.

BATTERSEA ARTS CENTRE BOOKSHOP
Old Town Hall, Lavender Hill, London SW11 5TF. 071-223 6557

Subjects: General, the arts.
Hours: Tue 10.00 - 6.00. Wed - Sat 10.00 - 8.00. Sun 12.00 - 6.00.
Services: Special orders, credit cards.

The old Town Hall is used as a theatre now and a large room is made over to the sale of books. While the arts are well represented this is essentially a local community bookshop, with general subjects and fiction; also women's and children's books.

THE BOLINGBROKE BOOKSHOP
147 Northcote Road, London SW11 6QB.   **071-223 9344**

Subjects: General, travel, children.
Hours: Mon - Sat 9.30 - 6.00. Thu 9.30 - 7.00.
Services: Special orders, credit cards.

Recently refurbished and expended, this is an attractive corner shop with a spiral staircase inside (not for public use). They classify their stock as 'middle of the road' and keep a good travel and children's section, also a new publications section. In an area of book stalls and bargain bookshops this deserves to prosper.

ADDISONS
137 Balham High Road, London SW12 9AY.   **081-675 1143**

Subjects: General paperbacks and remainders.
Hours: Mon - Sat 8.30 - 6.00.
Services: Special orders.

Half bookshop, half newsagents, the stock is popular paperback and some remaindered hardbacks. There is a small section of G.C.S.E. revision titles.

BEAUMONTS BOOKS
60 Church Road, Barnes, London SW13 ODQ.   **081-741 0786**

Subjects: General.
Hours: Mon - Sat 9.00 - 6.00.
Services: Special orders, credit cards.

Now open on two floors and completely refurbished, this shop caters for a wide range of tastes from the latest bestsellers through to children's, cookery, gardening, interior design, art, health and diet and travel books. They will order any book in print which is not in stock and aim to provide a very rapid service.

RAZZALL'S RIVERSIDE BOOKS
36A Barnes High Street, Barnes, SW13 9LP.   **081-878 7859**

Subjects: General, local history.
Hours: Mon, Wed, Fri 9.00 - 6.00. Thu 9.00 - 7.00. Tue, Sat
9.00 - 5.30.
Services: Special orders, credit cards.

Barnes is one of those enclaves of middle class civilization which dot the south west of London and manage to concentrate some worthwhile shops together of which this is one. The literary pages of the Sunday papers and weekly magazines are probably the main stimulus for buying new titles and they are sure to be found here. If not, the owner is in frequent contact with publishers in order to maintain stocks and meet demands. The proprietor is a literary man and so the standard of book selection is good.

GORDONS
8-9 High Street, Barnes, London SW13 9LW.   **081-878 1181**

Subjects: General.
Hours: Mon - Sat 9.00 - 5.30. Wed 9.00 - 1.00.
Services: Credit cards.

The shop sells popular paperbacks, cookery and children's books but these are rather a sideline to the selling of stationery and greetings cards.

VANDELEUR ANTIQUARIAN BOOKS
69 Sheen Lane, London SW14 8AD.

081-393 7752
081-878 6837

Subjects: General, antiquarian and secondhand.
Hours: Mon - Fri 2.00 - 7.30. Sat 11.30 - 7.30 - but changeable, advisable to phone.
Services: Mail order - catalogue, wants list.

A small shop selling books priced from 50p to £2500, particularly on natural history, travel and exploration, topography, mountaineering and big game hunting. Also chess, cricket, golf, rowing and other sports. The shop has one of the largest stocks of nineteenth century rowing prints in the country plus unusual subjects such as occult etc. as well as illustrated books and fine bindings. The owner is a helpful guide to the stock, which is backed up by a large reserve stock, but it is advisable to phone first as he is often out book hunting himself. He exhibits at rowing meetings and at the Provincial Booksellers Fairs Association book fairs.

AT THE SIGN OF THE DRAGON
131/133 Sheen Lane, London SW14 8AE.

081-876 3855

Subjects: General, science fiction, fantasy, children's books.
Hours: Mon - Sat 10.00 - 6.00. Wed 10.00 - 1.30.
Services: Special orders, credit cards, mail order, catalogue.

Space and time travellers would do well to arrive here. The shop makes a speciality of those alternative modes of transport and imagination, which seem to have a hold on the contemporary reader, who perhaps despairs of the more mundane probabilities on offer. Comics and magazines are also stocked.

RICHARD WORTH
Putney Books,
7-9 Lower Richmond Road, Putney,
London SW15 1JN.

081-788 9006

Subjects: General, politics, feminism.
Hours: Mon 12.00 - 6.00. Tue - Sat 10.00 - 6.00.
Services: Special orders, credit cards.

The shop is just around the corner from Putney High Street, facing the river. They have a good general range of new books with politics and sociology well represented.

W.H. SMITH LTD.
111 Putney High Street, London SW15 1SS.   **081-788 2573**

Subjects: General.
Hours: Mon - Sat 8.30 - 5.30.
Services: Special orders, credit cards.

This is a large WHS, centrally situated in this remarkably busy High Street. The ground floor has the stationery items and magazines, but
stretches back to a well stocked record and cassette department.
The first floor is a very large room — hall might be a better word — jam packed with books of every description, both in the wall fixtures and on the central display tables. This is clearly the bookshop for Putney and a first class WHS shop.

Putney High Street, as everybody knows, should be three times its present width and parking is a fearsome problem, but somehow trade seems to thrive in this community, lying just west of its very handsome Thames crossing.

Streatham - Tooting - Tooting Bec

PRATTS
210 Streatham High Road, London SW16 1BD.   **081-769 4450**

Subjects: Children's
Hours: Tue, Thu, Fri, Sat 9.00 - 5.30. Wed 9.30 - 7.30. Mon closed.

The book department is adjacent to the toy department and stocks books and story tapes for children of all ages. There is a restaurant on the second floor. Pratts is a branch of the John Lewis Partnership.

W.H. SMITH LTD.
180-182 Streatham High Road,
London SW16 1BH.   **081-677 3031/2**

Subjects: General.
Hours: Mon - Sat 8.30 - 5.30. Tue 9.30 - 5.30.
Services: Special orders, credit cards.

One of the larger Smiths stocking a good range of books. It has recently been refurbished and the books are now on display in a gleaming white area near the news and travel departments. The staff offer helpful advice.

WALTONS
15-17 Streatham High Road, London SW16 1DS.   **071-763 3334**

Subjects: General.
Hours: Mon - Fri 7.00 - 6.00. Sat 8.00 - 6.00.
Services: Special orders.

This is a large stationers and confectioners with a small selection of paperbacked books and atlases.

VILLAGE BOOKS
17 Shrubbery Road, Streatham,
London SW16 2AS.   **081-677 2667**

Subjects: General, new, secondhand and antiquarian.
Hours: Mon - Sat 10.30 - 7.00. Wed closed.
Services: Special orders, mail order, monthly book fair.

An interesting shop just off Streatham High Road dealing in a general range of new, secondhand and antiquarian books. For the size of shop they carry a surprisingly large number of titles, more than half of which are non-fictional. On the first Sunday of each month a book fair is held in the shop.

J. & G. BOOKS
17 Streatham Vale, London SW16 5SE.   **081-764 4669**

Subjects: New and secondhand natural history specialising in reptiles.
Hours: Mon - Fri 10.00 - 6.00. Sat 10.00 - 5.00. Closed Wed.
Services: Mail order (lists for new books).

Books on reptiles next to a shop stocking the real thing, so if closed call next door as both shops have the same owner. A few books on natural history and an increasing stock of editions on gemstones but books on snakes and other reptiles dominate the shelves.

ALPHA BOOK SHOP
193 Streatham High Road, London SW16 6EG.   **081-677 3740**

Subjects: General, secondhand.
Hours: Mon - Sat 10.00 - 7.00.
Services: Book exchange.

A general book shop stocking mainly popular titles including science fiction, westerns, war biographies, romances, and thrillers as well as some literature and study/text books. There are magazines on the martial arts, body building, boxing etc. They specialise in back number and out of print magazines but carry current issues as well. There is a half-back credit system in operation for the books. The shop is two minutes' walk from St Leonard's Church.

MANNA CHRISTIAN CENTRE
149 Streatham High Road,
London SW16 6EG.   **081-769 8588**

Subjects: Christian literature.
Hours: Mon - Sat 9.30 - 5.30.
Services: Special orders.

This shop stocks a comprehensive range of Evangelical Christian literature; Bibles, Sunday school books, devotional literature and a supporting range of tapes, records and cassettes. A bright and friendly shop where those in need can drop in for a chat or a little counselling, and with a coffee shop adjacent.

WORDS WORTH BOOKS
308 Streatham High Road,
London SW16 6HG.   **081-667 7872/9241**

Subjects: General, remainders and Black authors.
Hours: Mon - Fri 9.00 - 7.30. Sat 9.00 - 6.00.
Services: BBIP on CDRom, special orders, school, college and library supply, credit cards.

A double-fronted shop on the busy London-Brighton road, well-laid out and with helpful staff. Recently opened, it has developed the business by paying attention to customers' requests. It specialises in quality fiction and Black authors and carries a wide stock that is usually sufficiently varied to meet the needs of the city centre refugee. The pun inherent in the name reflects a surprising range of quality remainders.

SWANS BOOKSHOP
No. 5 Tooting Market,
Tooting High Street, London SW17 ORH.   **081-672 4980**

Subjects: General.
Hours: Mon - Fri 9.00 - 5.30 (closed Wed)
Services: Exchange of half priced paperbacks.

The setting of new and secondhand paperbacks as well as the book exchange side of things has been going on here for twenty years, which speaks of some success.

RUPOSHI BANGLA LTD.
220 Tooting High Street,   **081-672 7843**
London SW17 OSG.   **081-682 1718**

Subjects: Bengali language and literature from Bangladesh and West Bengal, India.
Hours: Mon - Sat 10.00 - 5.30.
Services: Special orders, mail order, catalogue, library and school supply.

This company specialises in books in Bengali and English on or from Bangladesh and West Bengal, State of India. They cover all subjects from language courses to research materials. Retail bookselling is only a part of their business as they provide a cataloguing service and can rebind books for libraries if required. They are also wholesalers and exporters, and run a translation service.

BECKETT'S BOOKSHOP
6 Bellevue Road, London SW17 7EG.   **081-672 4413**

Subjects: General.
Hours: Mon-Sat 10.00 - 6.00.
Services: Credit cards, special orders.

This attractive new bookshop overlooking Wandsworth Common has a wide range of general books and a well stocked children's section.

STRANGENESS AND CHARM
15 Trinity Road, Tooting Bec, London SW17 7SD. 081-767 5356

Subjects: Fantasy, fantasy art, science fiction, esoteric.
Hours: Tue - Sat 10.00 - 5.30 (variable).
Services: Tarot readings.

This bookshop has a fairly small selection of books on fantasy, science fiction and esoteric subjects and a collection of imported curios, some of which are arranged on the bookshelves with the books.

BOOKSPREAD/CHILDREN'S DISCOVERY CENTRE
58 Tooting Bec Road, London SW17 8BE.   081-767 6377/4551

Subjects: Children's books.
Hours: Mon - Fri 10.00 - 5.00. Thu 10.00 - 9.00. Sat 10.00 - 3.00.
Services: Mail order, special orders, stor telling, reading advisory service, exhibitions and even s.

An orange painted front marks this from other houses in the road and though one has to ring a bell to enter don't be put off as this is a most comprehensive bookshop and centre for children from 0-18 years. The stock includes multi-cultural, equal opportunities and dual language books. Story telling goes on, visits from authors and much else to encourage the reading habit. A newsletter of events is produced every two months — send s.a.e. for latest one. Help and advice is available from qualified staff.

STEPHEN FOSTER
213 Garratt Lane, Wandsworth,
London SW18 4DS. 081-877 0782

Subjects: General, secondhand, some antiquarian.
Hours: Mon - Sat 10.30 - 6.00. Closed Wed.
Services: Credit cards, special orders (new books).

This bookshop has a small general secondhand stock with a few antiquarian books. New books may be ordered. Parking outside is easy.

W.H. SMITH LTD.
69 Centre Mall, Arndale Shopping Centre,
Wandsworth, London SW18 4TG. 081-877 1979

Subjects: General.
Hours: Mon - Sat 9.00 - 6.00.
Services: Special orders, credit cards.

Located in the Arndale Centre, this is a long, spacious shop with the refreshing white decor that is now standard in most of the W.H. Smith stores. A good range of books in all general areas with paperback fiction prominent.

BOOKSTOP
127 Arndale Centre, London SW18 4TQ. 081-877 0783

Subjects: General, remainders.
Hours: Mon - Sat 9.00 - 5.30.
Services: Special orders, credit cards.

This is mainly a bargain bookshop with the emphasis on remainders but popular titles in hardback and paperback are stocked.

PLUS BOOKS LTD.
19 Abbey Parade,
Merton High Street, London SW19 1DG. 081-542 1665

Subjects: Secondhand paperbacks.
Hours: Mon - Sat 9.00 - 6.00.
Services: Book exchange.

A large stock of secondhand books and magazines to buy or exchange from.

SHERRATT & HUGHES
Unit 2, Wimbledon Bridge Development
Wimbledon, London SW19.   **081-543 9899**

Subjects: General, academic.
Hours: Mon - Fri 8.00 a.m. - 8.00 p.m. Sat 9.00 - 6.00.
Services: Mail order, professional accounts, school supply,
              seasonal catalogues.

This is the newest branch of Sherratt & Hughes, bringing modern, expert bookselling to Wimbledon. The shop is conveniently located opposite the station, with opening hours to suit passing commuters. Trading from two floors, the shop offers an extensive range of general stock. Emphasis is placed on paperbacks, green issues, art and interiors, children's and academic books, particularly English as a foreign language. The standard of service is very high and special attention is given to customer orders. Greetings cards and spoken word cassettes are also stocked.

NATIONAL SCHIZOPHRENIA FELLOWSHIP BOOKSHOP
5 Victoria Crescent, Wimbledon,
London SW19 1LG.   **081-542 2665 (home)**
Subjects: General, secondhand.
Hours: Mon - Sat 10.00 - 4.00.

This bookshop is a charity, with all stock being donated by the public and proceeds going to support the cause. The staff work on a voluntary basis. Because of the way the stock is procured it could be quite a good place for 'finds'. Everything is clearly headed and the variety is surprising.

THE LITTLE BOOKSHOP
39b The Broadway, Wimbledon,
London SW19 1QD.   **081-543 1031**

Subjects: General.
Hours: Mon - Sat 9.30 - 6.00.
Services: Special orders.

It is a small shop but the available space has been imaginatively adapted to hold a generally literary stock, with poetry and drama to the fore, but general books and a good children's section are also available.

ELYS P.L.C.
16 St. George's Road, Wimbledon,
London SW19 4DP.   **081-946 9191**

Subjects: General.
Hours: Mon - Fri 9.00 - 5.30. Sat 9.00 - 6.00.
Services: Special orders, credit cards.

Elys is a department store and books have part of the ground floor
to display themselves. Mostly popular stuff with current T.V. titles
prominently displayed on tables. Atlases, guides and dictionaries
well represented.

THE BOOKCELLAR
87 High Street, Wimbledon Village,
London SW19 5EF.   **081-946 0198**

Subjects: General, reference, art.
Hours: Mon - Sat 9.30 - 5.30. Wed 9.30 - 1.00.
Services: Special orders, credit cards.

Located in Wimbledon Village, this shop has a large selection of
books in the basement, with the emphasis on art and 'gift' books.
The service is friendly and knowledgeable.

CHILDREN'S BOOKSHOP
66 High Street, Wimbledon Village,
London SW19 5EE.   **081-947 2038**

Subjects: Books for children up to 16 years old.
Hours: Mon - Sat 9.00 - 5.30.
Services: Credit cards, special orders, school supply, mail order.

Catering for children and parents bringing up children, this bright
red fronted bookshop in Wimbledon Village is a joy to visit with its
cheery atmosphere. Shelves of both paper and hardback books
backed by tapes are arranged in age with a rear room devoted to
the 'under fives' with many cloth books, reading schemes and
scattered toys to keep the toddlers amused. Helpful and interested
assistance is at hand making this shop well worth a trip to visit.

W.H. SMITH LTD.
Wimbledon Station, London SW19 7NL.   081-946 6143

Subjects: General.
Hours: Mon - Fri 6.30 - 6.30. Sat 8.00 - 5.00.
Services: Special orders, credit cards.

This is quite a good little station bookshop with opening hours to suit the newspaper reader and commuter. Quite spacious and easy to look around.

FIELDERS
54 Wimbledon Hill Road, Wimbledon,
London SW19 7PA.   081-946 5044

Subjects: General, educational, guides and maps, children's, sheet music.
Hours: Mon - Sat 9.00 - 5.30.
Services: Special orders, credit cards, educational supply.

One enters apparently a stationers but upstairs is a huge, well supplied general book department. The paperback section is excellent and is well supported by a comprehensive range of hard backed titles. The travel and map section is one of the more prominent ones and carries a stock of Ordnance Survey maps.

KINGS BOOKS
28 Queens Road, Wimbledon,
London SW19 8LR.   081-947 2982

Subjects: Christian literature.
Hours: Mon - Sat 10.00 - 5.00. Wed 10.00 - 1.00.
Services: Special orders, church supplies and bookstalls.

This new, bright two-storey shop is attached to modern church premises and includes in its stock cassettes, compact discs and greetings cards. The books are arranged under subject: Christian life, devotional etc. and include a substantial children's section. There is wheelchair access and some free car parking spaces.

JOHN LEWIS P.L.C.
279-306 Oxford Street, London W1A 1EX.   **071-629 7711**

Subjects: Children's books.
Hours: Mon - Fri 9.00 - 5.30. Thu 9.30 - 8.00. Sat 9.00 - 5.30.
Services: John Lewis cards.

The children's books make a pleasant extension to the toy
department on the fourth floor, imaginatively displayed and easy
for youngsters to see. The sections are headed 'First Reading',
'Classics', etc.

BBC SHOP
**4/5 Langham Place, Upper Regent Street,
London W1A 4WW.**   **071-927 4970**

Subjects: BBC Publications
Hours: Mon - Fri 9.00 - 5.30. Sat 9.30 - 5.30.
Services: Special orders, catalogue, credit cards.

This is the London showroom for BBC Enterprises goods. They
stock the complete range of books, records, tapes and videos. As
well as the BBC publications there are books associated with BBC
programmes.

THE SCRIPTURE UNION BOOKSHOP
5 Wigmore Street, London W1H OAD.   **071-493 1851**

Subjects: Christian literature.
Hours: Mon, Tue, Fri, Sat 9.00 - 5.30. Wed 9.30 - 5.30. Thu
               9.00 - 7.00.
Services: Special orders, mail order, church bookstalls.

This double-fronted, stone faced shop is just around the corner
from Cavendish Square. Inside it is quite large, brightly lit and there
is plenty of room for browsing. The books are arranged under
specialist headings: Doctrine, Christian life, etc. There is an
impressive cabinet display of Bibles and prayer books and they also
sell records, videos and greetings cards.

DILLONS THE BOOKSTORE
(Educational and Children's),
37 Upper Berkeley Street, London W1H 8AS.   **071-706 3040**

Subjects: Infant and primary education, general children's books.
Hours: Mon - Fri 9.00 - 7.00. Sat 9.30 - 5.30.
Services: Special orders, mail order, lists, institutional supply, customer accounts, credit cards.

Another specialist Dillons bookstore, Dillons Educational and Children's is, as its name implies, a bookshop catering solely for the educational and children's markets. Now in operation since 1988, Dillons Educational is run by six experienced staff who supply books for all ages ranging from pre-school children to A-level students and their teachers. Mail order to schools and institutions is welcomed.

B.A. SEABY LTD.
8 Cavendish Square, London W1M 0AJ.   **071-580 3677**

Subjects: Numismatics.
Hours: Mon - Fri 9.30 - 5.00
Services Credit cards.

Primarily a dealer in coins and antiquities, Seaby also sell their own publications on numismatics and related archaeology. The stock is small but highly specialised.

SELFRIDGES (BOOK DEPARTMENT)   071-629 1234
400 Oxford Street, London W1M 1AB.   **Extn. 3152**

Subjects: General.
Hours: Mon - Sat 9.30 - 6.00. Thu 9.30 - 8.00.
Services: Special orders, mail order, credit cards.

A well designed, open plan department on the first floor of this famous store; for its size extremely well stocked. Paperback fiction and classics are the most extensive sections, though coverage is comprehensive and cookery and travel are particularly good.

CHRISTOPHER FOSS
120 Baker Street, London W1M 1LD.   **071-935 9364**

Subjects: General, travel, maps.
Hours: Mon - Fri 9.00 - 6.00. Sat 10.00 - 5.00.
Services: Special orders, credit cards, mail order.

On the ground floor stationery, downstairs books. The book department is small but is a mine of good things. The service is attentive. The shop will be closing some time in 1990 but the management intends to continue business in new premises.

THE CHIMES MUSIC SHOP
44 Marylebone High Street,   **071-935 1587**
London W1M 3AD.   **071-486 1303**

Subjects: Music, sheet music.
Hours: Mon - Fri 9.00 - 5.30, Sat 9.00 - 4.00.
Services: Mail order, record tokens, book tokens.

It is no accident that the Royal Academy of Music and Trinity College are only a trumpet blast away. The paraphernalia of the trade is on display in the window. The shop, recently moved from No. 65, is stocked with shelves of sheet music, standard reference books, cassettes and CDs.

GREEN'S BOOKSHOP
17 Marylebone High Street, London W1M 3PD.   **071-935 7227**

Subjects: General.
Hours: Mon - Fri 9.00 - 6.00. Sat 9.00 - 1.00.
Services: Special orders, credit cards.

A long-established newsagents who have recently entered the book trade. The books are downstairs, the stock general, including the latest hardbacks, paperback fiction, reference, children's books, maps and guides.

DAUNT BOOKS
83 Marylebone High Street, London W1M   **071-224 2295**

Subjects: Travel and General

Impressive new bookshop with stock (travel guides, travel narratives, photo books and novels) arranged geographically.

WHOLEFOOD BOOKS
24 Paddington Street, London W1M 4DR.　　　**071-935 3924**

Subjects: Nutrition, health, wholefood and vegetarian cookery, natural childbirth, organic farming, alternative therapies.
Hours: Mon 8.45 - 6.00. Tue - Fri 8.45 - 6.20. Sat 8.45 - 1.00.
Services: Special orders, mail order, catalogues, credit cards, delivery service in London.

Since its move the Wholefood Shop has improved its book section at the rear. The subjects are the same but more attractively displayed
with green the predominant colour and books for the health enthusiast. They also carry a range of journals and magazines, many of which, like the books, are of US origin and otherwise difficult to obtain.

UNDER TWO FLAGS
4 St. Christopher's Place,
Wigmore Street, London W1M 5HB.　　　**071-935 6934**

Subjects: Military uniforms.
Hours: Tue - Sat 10.00 - 5.00.
Services: Mail order.

In this fascinating narrow street are many unusual shops including this one which specialises in model soldiers. To complement this they have a section of books on military uniforms.

M. & R. GLENDALE
9a New Cavendish Street, London W1M 7RN.　　　**071-487 5348**

Subjects: General secondhand and antiquarian, Victoriana, illustrated, children's.
Hours: Mon - Fri 10.00 - 6.00.
Services: Books bought, mail order.

This shop (the entrance to which, despite the address, is in Marylebone Street) specialises in Victoriana, illustrated and children's books, and has a considerable collection of old Valentine and Christmas cards. They also carry a general secondhand book stock downstairs.

E. JOSEPH IN ASSOCIATION WITH CHAS. J. SAWYER
Third Floor, 1 Vere Street,   071-493 8353/4/5/3180
London W1M 9HQ.   Fax 071-629 5441

Subjects: Antiquarian, fine and rare books including English literature, colour plate books, fine bindings, Africana, Churchilliana and library sets in leather and cloth.
Hours: Mon - Fri 9.30 - 5.30 or by appointment.
Services: Mail order, catalogue, credit cards.

The amalgamation of two family bookselling businesses established during the nineteenth century. The office premises have the disadvantage of a lift but the advantage of splendid rooms lined with fine books and antique tables and chairs to make viewing a pleasure.

English literature is a strong subject but sets, private presses and illustrated books are all here; books on Africa and books on and by Winston Churchill are two important sections among the excellent stock.

R.I.B.A. BOOKSHOP
66 Portland Place, London W1N 4AD.   071-251 0791

Subjects: Architecture.
Hours: Mon - Fri 9.30 - 5.30.
Services: Special orders, international mail order, catalogue, recommended reading lists, magazine subscriptions, credit cards.

This shop, within the premises of the Royal Institute of British Architects (off the foyer) sells books from all parts of the world on architecture and related subjects: planning, landscape architecture, building and construction, graphics and management, including the Institute's own publications. The stock is attractively displayed and clearly sectioned.

KIMPTON'S MEDICAL BOOKSHOP
205 Great Portland Street,   071-580 6833
London W1N 6LR.   Fax 071-636 1649

Subjects: Medical.
Hours: Mon - Fri 9.00 - 5.30. Sat 9.30 - 5.00.
Services: Special orders, mail order, catalogue, credit cards.

The arrangement inside is rather library-like but the stock of medical books is well laid out and marked. They also sell medical instruments. A shop for the profession.

CAMBRIDGE HOUSE BOOKSHOP
28 Market Place, Oxford Circus,
London W1N 7AL.   **071-242 5577**

Subjects: English as a foreign language.
Hours: Mon - Fri 10.00 - 4.00.
Services: Special orders, international mail order.

The shop is inside a language school but is also open to the public. There is a large stock of books from many publishers for students and teachers of English as a foreign language. These are backed up by cassettes. Videos may be supplied on request.

VIRGIN MEGASTORE   **071-631 1234**
28-30 Oxford Street, London W1N 7AP.   **Ext. 222**

Subjects: Music biography, music reference, music instruction, art, cinema, humour, fiction, graphic art, graphic novels.
Hours: Mon - Sat 9.30 - 8.30. Tue 10.00 - 8.00.

Recently expanded and re-situated within this enormous record store, the Megastore Bookshop has a reputation for stocking practically all the rock biographies, reference manuals and album sheet music currently in print — from Abba to ZZ Top. Along with these, the department has more conventional jazz, classical, cinema and music instruction sections. In accordance with the varied tastes of the Megastore's customers, they also provide for the humorist, science-fiction and cult fiction readers, Freak Brothers' fans, budding graphic artists and (judging by the popularity of the books on body art, cult TV and tattooing) the downright strange. There is a separate shop selling comics on the first floor.

MOWBRAYS BOOKSHOP   **071-580 2812**
28 Margaret Street, London W1N 7LB.   **071·580 8614**

Subjects: General, theology.
Hours: Mon - Fri 9.00 - 6.00. Sat 9.30 - 5.00.
Services: Special orders, mail order, catalogues (Mowbrays Journal), credit cards.

This shop is situated north east of Oxford Circus, has four floors of books and is one of the half dozen or so really good general bookshops in Central London. The display of books on the ground floor will delight the browser as they are arranged in three-sided compartments by subject, providing areas of privacy. The ample paperback department is downstairs and they have added a computer section to their general subjects. Christian literature is well represented and they have theology and children's departments in the gallery. As well as books they sell church requisites, records of sacred music and greetings cards.

HEALTHWISE BOOKSHOP
(THE FAMILY PLANNING ASSOCIATION)
27-35 Mortimer Street, London W1N 7RJ.   **071-636 7866**

Subjects: Sexuality, contraception, sex education, women's health, AIDS/HIV.
Hours: Mon - Fri 9.30 - 5.00. Sat closed.
Services: Special order, mail order, book list.

A shop and showroom for professional people in the field as well as the layman. The books are well displayed, face-on, and include the Family Planning Association's own publications. Staff are on hand to help with selection of books.

R.D. FRANKS LTD.
Kent House, Market Place,   **071-636 1244**
(Great Titchfield Street), London W1N 8EJ.   **Fax 071-436 4904**

Subjects: International magazines, periodicals, text and reference books for fashion and allied trades, workroom equipment.
Hours: Mon - Fri 9.00 - 5.00.
Services: Mail order, catalogue, magazine subscriptions, credit cards.

A corner shop just behind Oxford Circus in the heart of London's fashion centre. Their large and international stock of fashion books and magazines must be unique, besides which they also sell the tools of the trade. Invaluable for manufacturers, designers, students, colleges, home dressmakers and anyone interested in fashion for men, women and children, textiles, display etc.

D.H. EVANS
318 Oxford Street, London W1N 9DA.   **071-629 8800**

Subjects: General.
Hours: Mon - Fri 9.30 - 6.00. Thu 9.30 - 8.00. Sat 9.00 - 6.00.
Services: Special orders, credit cards.

This general book department is on the fourth floor of the store. They mainly stock popular hard and soft backed books with some maps and guides.

W.H. SMITH LTD.
The Plaza on Oxford Street,
120 Oxford Street, London W1N 2DP.   **071-436 6282**

A very large W.H. Smith with about half of its floor-space devoted to books. There is a substantial general range of books in stock, including a large fiction section and a children's section. Recently-published titles are displayed on a book tower near the main entrance.

PILOT SOFTWARE LTD.
32 Rathbone Place, London W1P 1AD.   **071-636 2666**

Subjects: Business and home computers.
Hours: Mon - Fri 9.30 - 6.00. Sat 9.30 - 5.00.
Services: Special orders.

A wide selection of books on business software and advanced business applications.

INDEX BOOK CENTRE (INDEXREACH LTD.)
28 Charlotte Street, London W1P 1HJ.   **071-636 3532**

Subjects: General, politics, history, philosophy, economics.
Hours: Mon - Fri 9.00 - 7.00. Sat 10.00 - 5.00.
Services: Special orders.

At the front a general bookshop, specialisms at the back. Its particular strengths are socialist literature in paperback and women's studies; also good on literature and the media. There is a secondhand labour history and politics section.

POLLOCK'S TOY MUSEUM
1 Scala Street, London W1P 1LT.   **071-636 3452**

Subjects: Books on dolls and toys, theatres in book form.
Hours: Mon - Sat 10.00 - 5.00.
Services: Mail order, museum, toy theatre performances.

The museum shop is at street level and can be entered without paying to visit the Toy Museum, and what a wonderful trip into the past with old fashioned toys and books (all new) about toys and dolls and specially selected children's books. Cut out books to make theatres including the characters, with plays and Pollock's publications, make this a most unusual and fascinating shop — a far cry from the computers of today.

KIMPTONS MEDICAL BOOKSHOP
49 Newman Street, London W1P 4BB.   **071-580 4250**

Subjects: Medical.
Hours: Mon - Fri 9.30 - 5.30. Sat 9.30 - 1.30.
Services: Special orders, mail order, credit cards.

The one small room has the books arranged by subject with headings on the shelves. There is also a section on popular medicine for those not in the profession. The Middlesex Hospital opposite will cure most of your discovered maladies.

THE LITERARY GUILD BOOKSHOP
87 Newman Street, London W1P 4EN.   **071-637 0341 Ext 236**

Subjects: General.
Hours: Mon - Fri 10.00 - 6.00.
Services: Facility to join club and purchase at reduced prices, credit card.

A large, well-lit, carpeted showroom with well displayed books. One has to be a member of the club to purchase but one can sign up on the spot. There is an introductory offer of books at £1 each and a commitment to buy four more in the year at a reduced rate.

STAR BOOKS INTERNATIONAL
112 Whitfield Street, London W1P 5RU.   **071-388 9832**

Subjects: General (in English) and language books from Indian
sub-continent.
Hours: Mon - Fri 10.00 - 6.00.
Services: Mail order, catalogue, school and library supply.

Mainly a mail order business, this is also a showroom for teachers
and librarians. However, the public are also welcome to call in.
There is a large stock of dual-language children's books.

FRENCH'S THEATRE BOOKSHOP
52 Fitzroy Street, London W1P 6JR.   **071-387 9373**

Subjects: Theatre.
Hours: Mon - Fri 9.30 - 5.30.
Services: Special orders, catalogue, credit cards, sound effects
(catalogue), play licensing.

Pre-eminent among theatre bookshops, Samuel French's has been
established for 150 years but has moved to a corner site just behind
Warren Street tube station and will be missed in the Covent Garden
area. Their new premises are modern, lacking the heavy wood of the
old Southampton Street premises but they still have their
excellent range of British and American theatre books, covering
subjects from acting to direction, criticism to design, and plays from
all leading publishers in acting and reading editions. Also records
and cassettes.

PAPERCHASE
213 Tottenham Court Road, London W1P 9AF.   **071-580 8496**

Subjects: Art, children's.
Hours: Mon - Sat 9.00 - 6.00. Thu 9.00 - 7.00.
Services: Mail order if in stock, credit cards.

This quite large shop in Tottenham Court Road sells paper artifacts
from napkins to cut outs and decorations. A few art and children's
books are stocked.

BOOKS ETC.
222 Tottenham Court Road, London W1P 9AF.   **071-636 3270**

Subjects: General, computer books.
Hours: Mon - Fri 9.00 - 6.30. Thu 9.00 - 7.00. Sat 9.30 - 6.30.
Services: Special orders, mail order, credit cards.

Situated in the heart of London's specialist electronic and computer shopping centre, this branch of Books Etc. keeps an extensive range of computer books for both the business user and personal computer enthusiast. Paperback fiction, travel and business books are also well represented. Other general subjects are covered with thought to give all round variety. The staff are friendly and helpful.

BOOKCASE TOO
Roy Bloom Ltd.
121-2 Tottenham Court Road, London W1P 9HN   **071-387 9212**

Subjects: General, new paperbacks, remainders.
Hours: Mon - Fri 9.00 - 6.00. Sat 10.00 - 6.00.
Services: Credit cards.

An offshoot of the Ludgate Hill shop, stocking some new books but predominantly remainders.

VIRGIN AT MARBLE ARCH
527 Oxford Street, London W1R 1DD.   **071-491 8582**

Subjects: Music biography, sheet music, music reference, humour,
               science fiction, fantasy.
Hours: Mon - Sat 9.30 - 7.30. Thu 9.30 - 8.00.

The book department is on the first floor of the "new look" Virgin Megastore at Marble Arch. The department has a full range of music biographies and music folios which are ideal for those who wish to impress their friends with anything from Abba to Zappa and give a heartfelt rendition of their greatest hits. A selection of music reference books is available for the more serious minded of their customers who wish to expand their knowledge of jazz, blues, soul and psychedelia. Light relief is provided by the humour section, while those wanting to enter a new dimension could do worse than to take a look at the science fiction and fantasy books. In short, the book department offers a wide-ranging selection of the newest publications, reflecting the style of the shop as a whole.

CLAUDE GILL BOOKS
19-23 Oxford Street, London W1R 1RF.   **071-434 9759**

Subjects: General, remainders.
Hours: Mon - Sat 9.30 - 8.00.
Services: Book tokens, credit cards.

Enormous imitation books form the frontage of the Claude Gill shop in Oxford Street and inside its shelves and tables are attractively marked, making this an inviting shop to enter. Its stock covers most fields, in both paperback and hardback, with maps and guides near the entrance.

ATHENA BOOKS
119-121 Oxford Street, London W1R 1TF.   **071-734 3383**

Subjects: General.
Hours: Mon - Fri 9.30 - 8.00. Sat 10.00 - 8.00.
Services: Credit cards.

A new parade of quality shops on the east side of Oxford Circus includes a large branch of Athena with a spacious book department downstairs. The stock is described as upmarket but popular titles are well displayed with new titles in hardback. Gardening, cookery, music and a large fiction section have plenty of space and there is a selection of bargain books.

CLAUDE GILL BOOKS
10-12 James Street, London W1R 2AQ.   **071-629 8206**

Subjects: General.
Hours: Mon - Fri 9.30 - 8.00. Sat 9.30 - 6.00.

This shop has two entrances, one leading into the fascinations of St Christopher's Place. Claude Gill have spent time and money to up-date their shops making them bright and modern. This one is on two floors with plenty of room for their general section. They specialise in popular titles but do not neglect cookery, history and art. They belong to the Hatchards group of bookshops.

CHARLOTTE ROBINSON BOOKSHOP
35 Great Pulteney Street, London W1R 3DE.   071-437 3683

Subjects: Modern first editions, illustrated, children's.
Hours: Mon - Fri 11.00 - 6.00.
Services: Books bought, mail order, search service.

Five booksellers contribute to the excellent stock of this bookshop, recently renovated and now on two floors; Charlotte Robinson, Clearwater Books, Peter Jolliffe, Unicorn Books and Ming Books. Mainly literature, as the majority of stock is modern first editions, with children's and illustrated books prominent. Literature of the Great War is a speciality, and books by Henry Williamson are the favourite of Clearwater. Unicorn's field is 19th and 20th century children's and illustrated books. Ming Books specialise in detective fiction. A collector's bookshop with a welcoming atmosphere.

ACADEMY BOOKCLUB
51 Beak Street, London W1R 3LF.   071-437 2131/2

Subjects: Literature.
Hours: Mon - Fri 10.00 - 6.00.
Services: Facility to join club and purchase at reduced prices, credit cards.

This attractive 'shop' is actually the showroom of a literary bookclub, and displays their new titles with a selection of backlist. Membership, which is free, commits one to buying a minimum of four books a year, at prices which are some 25% below the published price.

ANDREW EDMUNDS
44 Lexington Street, London W1R 3LH.   071-437 8594

Subjects: Illustrated, antiquarian and rare books.
Hours: Mon - Fri 10.00 - 6.00. Appointment advisable.

Mainly a print shop but Andrew Edmunds does stock some rare books, art being one of the main subjects although illustrated books are the speciality.

JAPAN CENTRE
66-68 Brewer Street, London W1R 3PJ.　　　　**071-439 8035**

Subjects: Japanese language, Japanese magazines and books
Hours: Mon - Fri 10.00 - 8.00. Sat, Sun 10.00 - 6.00.
Services: Special orders, magazine subscriptions, mail order.

A lively centre on two floors which serves both the local community and Japanese expatriates. It houses an extensive range of Japanese language books, Japanese magazines and books on Japan, including travel guides, cookery, Japanese literature and martial arts. Help and advice from experienced staff is always available. The remainder of the shop is given over to a low-price Japanese restaurant, Japanese supermarket, travel agency and gifts.

BERNARD QUARITCH
5/8 Lower John Street,
Golden Square, London W1R 4AU.　　　　**071-734 2983**

Subjects: Antiquarian, rare books, manuscripts.
Hours: Mon - Fri 9.30 - 1.00, 2.00 - 5.30.
Services: Mail order, 10 catalogues per annum, valuation advice to collectors, auction services.

A rather awesome place, a minute's walk from Piccadilly Circus, with barred windows, security door and bags left with receptionist. The books are handsomely displayed against a green felt background with gold striplighting. There are eight specialist sections. Early printed books and medieval manuscripts, natural history, English literature, science and medicine, travel, philosophy and human sciences, the arts, and Near and Middle Eastern books and manuscripts. A pedigree amongst the antiquarians: anyone who has attended the London auction houses will have seen Quaritch's at the forefront in bidding for the fine and rare books. Founded by Bernard Quaritch from Göttingen in 1847.

LIBERTY & CO. (BOOK DEPARTMENT).
210-220 Regent Street, London W1R 6AH.　　　　**071-734 1234**

Subjects: Art, design.
Hours: Mon - Sat 9.30 - 6.00. Thu 9.30 - 7.30.
Services: Special orders, mail order, credit cards, book signing.

There is quite a small book department in this large, exclusive store of world repute. The easiest access to the books is from the Great Marlborough Street entrance. They specialise in art and design. The building is in the Tudor style, half timbered, with the coats of arms of Henry VIII's wives carved from the timbers of two men-of-war, H.M.S. Impregnable and H.M.S. Hindustan.

THE EUROPEAN BOOKSHOP LTD.
4 Regent Place, London W1R 6BH.   **071-734 5259**

Subjects: Books on and from Europe, European language books.
Hours: Mon - Fri 9.30 - 6.00. Sat 9.30 - 5.00.
Services Special orders for books in the main European languages.

Situated east off Regent Street, some 300 yards to the north of Piccadilly Circus. On the ground floor there is a wide range of French literature, course books, travel books, cookery books, etc. The basement houses books in other European languages and includes a section of self-tuition courses in many languages.

HAMLEY'S OF REGENT STREET LTD.
188-196 Regent Street, London W1R 6BT.   **071-734 3161**

Subjects: Children's books.
Hours: Mon - Fri 10.00 - 6.00. Thu 10.00 - 8.00. Sat 9.30 - 6.00.
Services: Mail order, special orders, credit cards.

The book section of this well renowned toy shop is on the first floor. It is a colourful department predominately for young children but there is a wide choice of fiction paperbacks suitable for the early teens.

BOOSEY & HAWKES MUSIC SHOP
295 Regent Street, London W1R 8JH.   **071-580 2060**

Subjects: Music, with emphasis on instrument playing.
Hours: Mon - Fri 9.00 - 5.00. Sat 9.00 - 1.00
Services: Special orders, mail order, credit cards.

The book section is at the rear of the shop. The emphasis of the books displayed is on performing the art and there is a wide selection of sheet music.

WISDOM PUBLICATIONS
23 Dering Street (2nd floor),
London W1R 9AA.   **071-499 0925**

Subjects: Buddhism, including manuscripts and teachings not available elsewhere.
Hours: Mon - Sat 9.30 - 6.00.
Services: Mail order, trade distribution catalogue, credit cards.

Wisdom's own publications can be seen here in an office atmosphere together with other publishers' titles on Buddhism. As they are classed as a charity it is run on a semi-voluntary basis and their aim is to help perpetuate the various traditions of Buddhism by presenting them in English in their various forms: theory and practice, biography, history, art and literature for children. They are situated in a small street opposite House of Fraser off Oxford Street and is worth making a lift journey to the second floor to receive courteous and enthusiastic advice on their extensive stock.

THOMAS E. SCHUSTER
The Schuster Gallery, 14 Maddox Street,   **071-491 2208**
London W1R 9PL.   **Fax 071-491 9872**

Subjects: Fine and rare colour plate books.
Hours: Gallery: Mon - Fri 10.00 - 5.30. Sat 10.00 - 2.00. Books viewed by appointment only.

Prints dominate this shop but they also do have some interesting antiquarian books on natural history. Colour plate and illustrated editions are their speciality.

ROYAL ACADEMY OF ARTS BOOKSHOP
Burlington House, Piccadilly, London W1V 0DS.   **071-439 7438**

Subjects: Art.
Hours: Mon - Sun 10.00 - 5.30.
Services: Mail order for exhibition catalogues.

The shop is at the top of the grand staircase. Besides books and catalogues it sells artists' materials and an interesting selection of products designed by Members and exclusive to the Royal Academy. They also have a large range of quality reproductions from current exhibitions or from their permanent collection, as well as more general books on art.

THE CRAFTSMEN POTTERS SHOP
William Blake House, 7 Marshall Street,
London W1V 1LP.   **071-437 7605**

Subjects: Books on pottery and ceramics.
Hours: Mon - Sat 10.00 - 5.30. Thu 10.00 - 7.00.
Services: Special orders, credit cards.

A fine selection of hand made pottery takes up the majority of space in this unusual shop but they have a section of books on all aspects of pottery for both the professional and the amateur. History of ceramics and techniques are among the aspects covered with plenty of space to browse.

GRANT & CUTLER LTD.
55 Gt Marlborough Street,   **071-734 2012**
London W1V 2AY.   **Fax 071-734 2013**

Subjects: Books in the major West European languages.
Hours: Mon - Fri 9.00 - 5.30. Sat 9.00 - 1.00.
Services: Special orders, mail order, institutional supply, catalogue, credit cards.

Off Regent Street, this is the largest specialist foreign-language bookshop in the country. Packed with over a hundred thousand books and cassettes in French, Spanish, German and Italian. Subjects covered include literature, literary criticism, translations, language teaching, reference, commerce, politics, economics, and social studies. There is an excellent specialist dictionary section.

SCHOTT & CO. LTD.
48 Great Marlborough Street, London W1V 2BN 071-437 1246/8

Subjects: Music, sheet music.
Hours: Mon - Fri 9.00 - 5.00.
Services: Credit cards.

Most of the stock is sheet music with a small section of books from various publishers on the theory of music and lists on musicology and individual composers.

QUARTET BOOKSHOP
45 Poland Street, London W1V 4AU.   **071-437 1019**

Subjects: General, jazz, photography, cinema.
Hours: Mon - Fri 10.00 - 6.00.
Services: Special orders, credit cards.

A small well-run bookshop near Oxford Circus which specialises in books on jazz, photography and the cinema. As part of Pipeline full sales chain, it is able to offer an extremely speedy customer order service, which is maintained by friendly and efficient staff.

ATHENA BOOKSHOP
Trocadero Centre, Coventry Street,
London W1V 7FE.   **071-734 5061**

Subjects: General.
Hours: Mon - Sun 10.00 am - 11.00 pm.
Services: Credit cards.

Athena have street frontage at this new centre near Piccadilly Circus and have two floors of books with subjects chosen to serve the general London public and tourists, who will find their long opening hours convenient. Traditional Athena stock is backed by (predominantly paperback) books, with young people particularly well catered for.

THE VINTAGE MAGAZINE SHOP
39-41 Brewer Street, London W1V 7HF.   **071-439 8525**

Subjects: Cinema and theatre, (mainly secondhand), magazines
              and children's annuals.
Hours: Mon - Fri 10.00 - 7.00. Sun 2.00 - 7.00.
Services: Credit cards.

Two floors of this shop are filled with magazines and books about movies and the theatre, taking a step back into the past with Picture Post, old Radio Times and bound volumes of magazines including The Strand. The books are mainly situated in the basement and it is an interesting trip amongst the memorabilia.

AUTOMOBILE ASSOCIATION BOOKSHOP
Fanum House, 5 New Coventry Street,
London W1V 8HT.   **081-891 9032**

Subjects: Motoring, guides, maps.
Hours: Mon - Fri 9.00 - 5.00. Sat 9.00 - 12.30.
Services: Credit cards.

This is the largest branch of the A.A. in Britain and here, besides all sorts of gadgets for the car, one can purchase a good range of guides, atlases and maps, also some titles of general interest on the countryside and places of interest.

HATCHARDS
187 Piccadilly, London W1V 9DA. **071-439 9921**

Subjects: General.
Hours: Mon - Fri 9.00 - 6.00. Sat 9.00 - 5.00.
Services: Special orders, mail order, catalogue, credit cards, out-of-print search service.

This shop has only one other possible rival in London to match its comprehensiveness and the expertise of its staff.

It was started in 1797 by John Hatchard with a capital of £5 and is now a Collins subsidiary with a £6m a year turnover. There are over 350,000 titles in stock, which will surprise those who judge it only by its small, attractive exterior. It is a prestigious shop, with four Royal Warrants, many signing sessions by famous authors, and it gives an 'author of the year' party for about 200 luminaries of the writing and publishing world. There are four levels to the shop.

In the basement are the paperbacks with the fiction arranged alphabetically by author around the walls, and there are tables with new titles and other specialities scattered throughout.

As they have acquired the shop next door, Hatchards have been able to expand many of their sections, particularly the travel and paperback department which now have very much more room. The shop may now be approached directly from the eastern street entry. At street level in the main premises current hardback fiction, biographies etc., at the front of the shop and at the back they keep the non-fictional titles — history, religion, reference and so on. On the first floor they have sport, gardening (huge!), art and other sections which are perhaps grouped for their illustrative or photographic suitability. The second floor has a wonderful children's section. One for classical literature and first editions department, with some of their treasures on display in cabinets.

THE BOURNEMOUTH ENGLISH BOOK CENTRE
(International House Bookshop)
106 Piccadilly, London W1V 9FL. **071-493 5226**

Subjects: English language teaching materials.
Hours: Mon - Fri 10.00 - 1.30. 2.30 - 6.00.
Services: Mail order (tel: 0202-715555). Special orders.

Pass through the busy foyer of International House to find an octangular room with a large range of books for English language teaching and learning, with a trained teacher in charge to give knowledgeable advice. Current and popular titles are kept in stock for teachers or students of English with a good dictionary section and cassettes to back the various courses.

CLAUDE GILL BOOKS
213 Piccadilly, London W1V 9LD.   **071-434 9617/8**

Subjects: General, paperback fiction, travel, business, language books.
Hours: Mon - Fri 9.00 - 7.00. Sat 10.00 - 7.00. Sun 11.00 - 7.00.
Services: Special orders, mail order, out-of-print advertising service (through Hatchards of Piccadilly), Spring and Autumn catalogues.

Strategically situated near Piccadilly Circus, this generously proportioned bookshop concentrates on popular lines over quite a large range of subjects and spans three floors. It has a wide range of new titles in paperback and hardback and is particularly strong on travel guides, paperback fiction, business and language books. There is a wide variety of greetings cards, and diaries and wrapping paper are also stocked. It is a member of the Hatchards group.

NIGEL GREENWOOD BOOKS
4 New Burlington Street, London W1X 1FE.   **071-434 3797**

Subjects: Books and catalogues on the contemporary arts.
Hours: Mon - Fri 10.00 - 6.00. Sat 10.30 - 1.30.
Services: Mail order, catalogue.

The bookshop is situated within the Nigel Greenwood Gallery on the ground floor, and carries a very extensive stock of books and catalogues. Photography, architecture and design, music, film and video art make up their speciality sections on the contemporary arts.

HENRY SOTHERAN
2,3,4 & 5 Sackville Street, London W1X 2DP   **071-734 1150**

Subjects: General, new and antiquarian, autograph letters, fine bindings, bibliography, ornithology.
Hours: Mon - Fri 9.30 - 6.00. Sat 10.00 - 2.00.
Services: Special orders, international mail order, catalogues, library supply, book binding, journal subscriptions, credit cards, book restoration.

The oak lined interior has the proper air of gravitas with its glass topped cabinets and shelves of leather bound books. Sotherans have a claim to be the oldest antiquarian booksellers in London where they opened in 1815. They were the purchasers of Charles Dicken's library (he was a customer) and part of Sir Winston Churchill's. The ornithological section is fine — from Gould prints to pocket guides — and they are the largest stockists of new ornithology books in London. Bibliophiles will know it and the passer by will be surprised at its catholicity. As purchasers of Weinreb architectural books they have the largest selection of the subject in London.

MUSEUM OF MANKIND BOOKSHOP
6 Burlington Gardens, London W1X 2EX.   **071-323 8045**

Subjects: Ethnography of non western cultures and societies, related children's books.
Hours: Mon - Sat 10.30 - 12.30. 1.30 - 4.30. Sun 3.00 - 5.45.
Services: Book lists for British Museum publications.

The Museum of Mankind is a department of the British Museum and is part of British Museum Retail. The bookshop stocks many of their publications relevant to the indigenous peoples of Africa, Australia, South and North America, parts of Asia and Europe and the Pacific Islands as well as exhibition-related titles.

CAPTAIN O.M. WATTS LTD.
45 Albermarle Street, London W1X 4BT.   **071-493 4633**

Subjects: Maritime books.
Hours: Mon - Fri 9.00 - 6.00. Thu 9.00 - 7.00. Sat 9.00 - 5.00.
Services: Mail order, catalogue.

A fascinating shop for anyone interested in yachts and all the bits and bobs that go with them. Just inside the entrance is their selection of books on sailing including navigation and some fiction, all to do with boats.

READERS DIGEST
22 Berkeley Square, London W1X 6AB.   **071-629 8144**

Subjects: Readers Digest publications plus other publishers' books on travel, reference and languages etc. including Time Life and children's books.
Hours: Mon - Fri 9.00 - 5.30.
Services: Special orders, mail order, catalogue.

Although the Readers Digest books are displayed here they have also a very good selection of unusual series, maybe difficult to find elsewhere: Time Life publications, a popular series of Library of Nations, also the 'Which' titles and an excellent travel and guide section. English language teaching series and dictionaries have their own corner, with an imaginative children's selection, gardening/cookery, keep fit and health all well displayed.

MAGGS BROS. LTD.
50 Berkeley Square,   **071-493 7160**
London W1X 6EL.   **Fax 071-499 2007**

Subjects: Antiquarian, early English literature, manuscripts, travel, miniature, fine bindings.
Hours: Mon - Fri 9.30 - 5.00.
Services: Book restoration, mail order, monthly catalogues by subject.

A family concern since 1850, these elegant premises on the west side of Berkeley Square are of world repute to all collectors. To call these deep carpeted rooms on three levels a shop doesn't quite catch the atmosphere of bibliophilic earnestness which you find. Photographs of the generations of Maggs line the staircase connecting the two levels, sanctifying the serious pursuit of the arcane and valuable.

ROWLAND WARD'S AT HOLLAND & HOLLAND
31 Bruton Street, London W1X 8JS.   **071-499 4411**

Subjects: Africa, natural history, field sports (new and antiquarian).
Hours: Mon - Fri 9.30 - 5.30.
Services: Special orders, mail order, lists.

Holland & Holland are gun manufacturers and the books here are in the basement of their London showroom. Besides books there is shooting clothing, plus accessories and gifts.

JONATHAN POTTER LTD.
21 Grosvenor Street,   **071-491 3520**
London W1X 9FE.   **Fax 071-491 9754**

Subjects: Original antique maps, atlases, engravings.
Hours: Mon - Fri 9.30 - 5.30. Sat and evenings by appointment.
Services   Mail order, illustrated catalogue, valuations, framing, paper restoration, credit cards.

A fine selection of original maps for sale. The stock covers London and all British counties, every part of the world, sea charts and celestials, with prices from about £50 upwards. Reference books on the history of cartography and map collecting.

CAISSA BOOKS (PUBLISHING) LTD.
Grays in the Mews (A18/19),
1-7 Davies Mews, London W1Y 1AR.   **071-409 7283**

Subjects: Chess, antiquarian, secondhand, new, in many languages.
Hours: Mon - Fri 11.00 - 6.00.
Services: Mail order, telephone order, 2-3 lists per year, credit cards.

The only chess specialist bookshop in Central London is to be found in the basement of Grays in the Mews close to Bond Street tube station. This company is also a publisher of books on chess and its publications have enjoyed considerable success and favourable reviews.

THE GOLFIANA & BOOK GALLERY
Sarah Baddiel, Gray's Antique Market, B12,   **071-408 1239**
Davies Mews, London W1Y 1LB.   **081-452 7243**

Subjects: Secondhand, specialising in golf, motoring, juvenile and illustrated books.
Hours: Mon - Fri 10.00 - 6.00.

Look for the indoor stream in Gray's Antique Market and you will find the small stall with books on golf, motoring/transport and some juvenile and illustrated books. Also pictures, prints, ephemera, ceramics, silver, clubs, tin and diecast toys.

JOHN O'CALLAGHAN
Stand J23-25, Gray's Antique Market,
Davies Mews (off Davies Street,) London W1Y 1LB.

Subjects: Art and architecture, monographs, reference (new and secondhand).
Hours: Mon - Fri 10.00 - 6.00.

The stand is mid-way along the building at street level. It offers a good selection of mainly out-of-print and some new books on art and architecture. Reference books on a comprehensive range of antiques are well represented. There are monographs on leading artists, architects and movements.

RUSSELL RARE BOOKS
Gray's Antique Market, 58 Davies Street,
London W1Y 1LB. 071-629 0532

Subjects: Antiquarian, travel, natural history, fine bindings, leather bound sets.
Hours: Mon - Fri 10.00 - 6.00.
Services: Credit cards.

A large, walk-in, self-contained stall in Gray's Antique Market accommodates these antiquarian books. There is a stock of about two thousand books ranging in price from about £25 to £5000.

G.HEYWOOD HILL LTD.
10 Curzon Street, London W1Y 7FJ. 071-629 0647

Subjects: General (new and secondhand), antiquarian, fine bindings, English literature, historical, children's books.
Hours: Mon - Fri 9.00 - 5.30. Sat 9.00 - 12.30.
Services: Special orders, international mail order, bookbinding.

An attractive, bow-windowed 18th century front sets the right tone for this rather prestigious shop. Founded only in 1936, it is already rich in association, often being mentioned in the diaries of Waughs, Mitfords, etc. Nancy Mitford ran the shop for three years from 1942. Inside, the shelves and tables groan with good, rare and beautiful things destined, one likes to imagine, for private libraries in country houses, where the spirit of letters may still flourish. Down some marginally perilous stairs there is a good show of children's books. The service here is knowledgeable and attentive.

TURF NEWSPAPERS LTD.
18 Clarges Street, London W1Y 7PG. 071-499 4391

Subjects: Horse racing, hunting, horse breeding, biographies associated with the turf.
Hours: Mon - Fri 9.00 - 5.00. Sat 9.00 - 12.00.
Services: Mail order, lists, subscriptions to U.K. and foreign newspapers and magazines.

This small showroom in Mayfair provides for the racing fraternity which has always been found in this area. All books equine are generously displayed and they also stock horserace videos.

MARLBOROUGH RARE BOOKS
144-146 New Bond Street, London W1Y 9FD.   **071-493 6993**

Subjects: Antiquarian, rare books, art, architecture, illustrated books before 1850.
Hours: Mon - Fri 9.30 - 6.00.
Services: Mail order, catalogue, advice on book collecting, valuation.

Very much for collectors and not casual browsers. Visitors are welcome but advised to phone first for an appointment. They specialise in the arts but also have photography, topography and natural history books.

CHAPPELL OF BOND STREET
50 New Bond Street, London W1Y 9HA.   **071-491 2777**

Subjects: Music.
Hours: Mon - Fri 9.30 - 6.00. Sat 9.30 - 5.00.
Services: Special orders, mail order, credit cards.

Among the pianos and other instruments Chappells stock a very large selection of popular and classical music. A vast range of music is covered and is catalogued under the instrument. A very efficient postal service is operated for U.K. and overseas customers, and credit card orders ensure same day despatch.

JOHN MENZIES (G.B.) LTD.
Paddington Concourse,
Paddington Station, London W2 1HB.   **071-723 3153**

Subjects: General.
Hours: Mon - Sun 7.00 - 10.00
Services: Credit cards.

Quite a large shop on Paddington Station with general stock under subjects, both paperback and hardback, with a strong section on railways. Glossy gift books and children's are available, with a couple of tables of remainders.

MODERN BOOK CO.
19/21 Praed Street, London W2 1NP.   **071-402 9176**

Subjects: Computing, medical, engineering, general.
Hours: Mon - Fri 9.00 - 5.30. Sat 9.00 - 1.00.
Services: Library supply, mail order, enquiry service available to check any book published in U.K. or U.S.A.

An impressive, large, brightly-lit shop at the Edgware Road end of Praed Street with an extensive window display. Inside, the sections are well marked and though the shop emphasises its technical books there are good sections on management, law, accountancy, economics and a good general section. The principal bookshop in this postal district and for some way beyond it.

HOSAINS
25 Connaught Street, London W2 2AY.   **071-262 7900**

Subjects: Antiquarian and secondhand books on the Middle East, North Africa, India, Tibet and Central Asia.
Hours: Tue - Fri 10.30 - 5.30. Sat 10.30 - 1.00.
Services: Mail order, catalogue, credit cards, search service.

Almost all the books are in English relating to their specialist regions with an excellent stock, well displayed and accessible for their customers, although mail order is a strong side of the business. Only books on their particular countries and continents are stocked, backed by manuscripts and miniatures related to those areas, but general subjects are represented, from religion, history to travel and art, with literature and illustrated books the largest section.

BAYSWATER BOOKS
27A Craven Terrace, London W2 3EL.   **071-402 7398**

Subjects: Antiquarian, general secondhand, modern first editions.
Hours: Mon at 11.00 - 7.00 (variable, but often much later).
Services: Search service, mail order, credit cards.

A one-man bookshop whose owner has achieved notable success in finding elusive and obscure titles. He has to hunt for these, which means that his hours are very flexible. To ensure a successful visit, therefore, it is advisable to telephone in advance to guarantee that the shop will be open. Bookshops are still thin on the ground in W2, but then so are book buyers; discerning bibliophiles have been heard shouting "Bonanza" on these premises

DAR AL DAWA BOOKSHOP
32 Hereford Road, London W2 4AJ.   **071-221 6256**

Subjects: Islamic, Arabic.
Hours: Mon - Sat 9.00 - 7.00.
Services: Special orders, exhibitions, university supply, mail order, magazine subscriptions.

Book in English and Arabic are stocked including books for children. They have a strong language section with reference titles mainly in English and Arabic. Islam and Middle Eastern history and affairs are the main subjects, and knowledgeable help is at hand.

UKRAINIAN BOOKSHOP
49 Linden Gardens,
Notting Hill Gate, London W2 4HG.   **071-229 0140**

Subjects: General subjects in Ukrainian.
Hours: Mon - Fri 9.00 - 12.30. 1.30 - 8.00. Sat 9.00 - 12.30.
Services: Mail order (lists). Special order. School and library supply.

One large room at the Association of Ukrainians in Great Britain is their bookshop with books on general subjects in Ukrainian backed by a few relevant books in English.

KELTIC
25 Chepstow Corner, Chepstow Place,
London W2 4TT. 071-229 8560/8456

Subjects: English language teaching.
Hours: Mon - Fri 10.00 - 5.30. Thu 10.00 - 7.00. Sat 10.00 - 1.00.
Services: International mail order, catalogues, supply to language
schools, seminars and talks.

With ground floor offices, one descends to the spacious, well-lit
basement showroom to get down to the business of selecting books.
There are chairs for browsers and the whole presents a pleasing
atmosphere.

BOOKS ETC.
Unit 16, Whiteleys of Bayswater,
Queensway, London W2 4YQ. 071-229 3865

Subjects: General.
Hours: Mon - Sat 9.30 - 8.00.
Services: Special orders, international mailing, credit cards.

A short distance from Queensway and Bayswater tube stations, this
stylish branch of Books Etc, is in the elegant Whiteleys shopping
centre. Occupying two floors, the shop has an excellent selection of
hardback and paperback fiction and non-fiction. There are readings
and other events for children, while parents can look through the
carefully selected stock in all subjects including business and
computer books, travel, art and other leisure interest books. There
is a very good range of foreign fiction, language books and dictionaries, books on tape and videos. They have a colourful card and
giftwrap section. This well-organised shop is run by helpful staff.

AL SAQI BOOKS
26 Westbourne Grove, London W2 5RH. 071-229 8543

Subjects: New, secondhand and out of print books on Islam, the
Arabian Peninsular and all areas of the Moslem world.
Hours: Mon - Sat 10.00 - 7.00.
Services: Special orders, mail order, catalogue, credit cards.

Books on Islam and the Middle East in English, and a large stock
of books in Arabic, which is probably the second language in the
Bayswater Road hinterland. They also publish in their subject area.

RED AND GREEN BOOKS LTD.
144 Churchfield Road, Acton, London W3 6BS.   **081-992 6029**

Subjects: General, women's writing, politics, non-sexist, non-racist, children's books, Open University (all courses).

Hours: Mon - Sat 9.00 - 6.00. Wed 9.00 - 2.00.

Services: Special orders, credit cards.

A bright, attractive bookshop offering friendly personal service. One of the few bookshops in West London stocking feminist, lesbian and gay, radical and Third World writing. They also stock quality fiction, biography etc. and greetings cards, postcards, recycled stationery and T-shirts. A coffee shop is planned for the near future.

GOOD NEWS
50 Churchfield Road, Acton, London W3 6DL.   **081-992 7123**

Subjects: Bibles, Christian books.

Hours: Mon - Thu 9.00 - 5.30. Fri 9.00 - 6.30. Sat 9.00 - 4.45.

Services: Discounts for church bookstalls, video hire, credit cards.

A Christian resource centre run by partners Scott and Lau. They stock a very large number of Bibles in many languages and a wide range of Christian books including renewal literature in which they specialise. Music and video cassettes and greetings cards are on offer. They are very close to Acton Central railway station.

W.A. FOSTER
134 and 183 Chiswick High Road,
London W4 1PU.   **081-995 2768**

Subjects: General, secondhand and antiquarian.

Hours: Mon - Sat 10.30 - 6.00.

Services: Books bought.

A good spread of books and prints here with bargains in boxes outside and the general stock ordered by subject together with antiquarian books on the inside.

FOUNTAIN BOOKS
229 Chiswick High Road, London W4 2DW.   **081-994 9500**

Subjects: General, children's.
Hours: Mon - Sat 9.30 - 6.00.
Services: Special orders, credit cards.

A bright, modern shop with an excellent stock of books in general subjects, heavy in art, psychology and health. The two floors enable them to carry a large fiction section down to an adequate stock of travel guides, providing a well needed service in Chiswick.

FAIRCROSS BOOKS
Strand Antiques, 166 Thames Road,
Strand-on-the-Green, London W4 3QS.   **081-994 1912**

Subjects: General, secondhand, remainders.
Hours: Mon - Sun 12.00 - 5.00.
Services: Out-of-print search service.

The shop is between Kew and Chiswick Bridges on the North bank of the Thames, opposite The Bull's Head. It occupies four floors and has a good general range of secondhand books and remainders as well as antiques, both large and small. A browser's paradise, but allow plenty of time to see it all.

W.H. SMITH LTD.
370 Chiswick High Road, London W4 5TA.   **081-995 9427**

Subjects: General.
Hours: Mon - Sat 9.00 - 6.00.
Services: Special orders, credit cards.

A medium-sized Smith's which covers the range of general books adequately and is probably well used as bookshops are thin on the ground in these parts.

G.L. GREEN
104 Pitshanger Lane, London W5 1QX.   **081-997 6454**

Subjects: Naval and maritime (new, secondhand, antiquarian).
Hours: Wed - Sat 10.00 - 5.00.
Services: Books bought, search service, international mail order.

An extensive stock of books, journals, magazines and postcards in their specialist area, displayed in three rooms on two floors. They also trade in cigarette cards, on all subjects and carry a general range
of books.

W.H. SMITH LTD.
21-23 The Broadway, Ealing, London W5 2NH.   **081-567 1471**

Subjects: General.
Hours: Mon - Sat 9.00 - 6.00. Thu 9.00 - 6.30
Services: Special orders, credit cards.

A very attractive spiral staircase leading to a basement of books in this large branch of W.H. Smith. They have an extensive stock, well laid out and more imaginatively displayed than in many other branches. Paper and hardbacks in most subjects with tables of books well displayed and brightly presented. The computer department upstairs carries additional book stock.

BOOK BARGAINS OF OXFORD LTD.
19 New Broadway, Ealing, London W5 2XQ.   **081-579 2990**

Subjects: General.
Hours: Mon - Fri 10.00- 6.00. Sat 9.30 - 5.30.
Services: Special orders, mail order, catalogue, 10-20% discount on purchases over £50, credit cards.

Specialises in a wide range of remaindered and end-of-line books at 50% or more off the publisher's recommended price. Many books are, in fact, much less than half-price. They will also order a range of full-priced books on request and offer a mail order service with a free colour catalogue for out-of-town and overseas customers.

O.C.S. BOOKSHOP
2 Grosvenor Parade, Ealing Common,
London W5 3NN.   **081-992 6335**

Subjects: Japanese.
Hours: Tue - Sat 10.00 - 6.00.
Services: Mail orders, special orders, newspapers in Japanese.

A bookshop for the Japanese with the majority of texts in Japanese, though some are in English. They sell three newspapers which are beamed over by satellite from Japan the same day.

CLAUDE GILL BOOKS
64 Ealing Broadway Centre,
The Broadway, London W5 5JY.   **081-840 5905**

Subjects: General.
Hours: Mon - Sat 9.30 - 6.00.
Services: Special orders, seasonal catalogues, search service for out-of-print books (via Hatchards), credit cards.

Ealing Broadway Centre is architecturally exceptional, unusual and imaginative. Claude Gill Books have a prime site here with two floors of books. It is well stocked and well staffed and has a pleasant atmosphere. Selling both hardbacks and paperbacks with some remainder books, it has a large children's section on the ground floor, and a good reference and study aid section downstairs. Other services offered include special customer orders, free seasonal catalogues, and a search service for out-of-print books, operated by Hatchards, for which there is a modest £1 charge. There is also a wide range of cards and gift wrap.

DILLONS THE BOOKSTORE
Ealing College of Higher Education,
St. Mary's Road, Ealing, London W5 5RF.   **081-579 4111**

Subjects: Academic texts.
Hours: Mon - Fri 9.00 - 5.00 (termtime only).
Services: Special orders, customer accounts, credit cards.

Dillons Bookstore is located on the campus of Ealing College primarily to supply students and faculty with a comprehensive variety of academic books. This small shop also appeals to local customers looking for specialist volumes which can be ordered.

Hammersmith

W.H. SMITH LTD.
Kings Mall, King Street,
Hammersmith, London W6 OPZ.   **081-748 2218**

Subjects: General.
Hours: Mon - Fri 9.00 - 5.45. Sat 9.00 - 6.00.
Services: Special orders, credit cards.

W.H. Smith have one large floor in this shopping mall with the majority of space given to their general book department, enabling their customers to meander amongst the displays of hard and paperback titles. To one side they have a selection of dictionaries, travel guides, reference books and students' notes, while the centre tables hold the glossy new titles and of course they have the ever popular children's and gardening/cookery sections.

HAMMICKS BOOKSTORE
9 Kings Mall, Hammersmith, London W6 0PZ.   **081-741 2467**

Subjects: General, children's.
Hours: Mon - Sat 9.00 - 5.30.
Services: Special orders, credit cards.

A pleasant, friendly bookshop offering approximately 15,000 titles in hardback and paperback which are arranged under subject headings. There is a special area for children's books. Other products sold include maps, greetings cards and talking books. Customer orders are welcomed and many can be supplied within 48 hours.

KSIEGARNIA S.P.K.
P.C.A. Publications Ltd.,
238 King Street, London W6 ORF.   **081-748 5522**

Subjects: Poland.
Hours: Tue - Fri 10.30 - 7.00. Sat 10.30 - 5.00.
Services: Special orders, international mail order, educational and
library supply.

The shop has a comprehensive stock of books in Polish and English on Poland, covering its literature, history and politics.

AUTOMOBILE ASSOCIATION
24 King Street, Hammersmith, London W6 OQW

081-748 0444
081-748 0555

Subjects: Motoring, guides and maps.
Hours: Mon - Sat 9.00 - 5.00.
Services: Travel agents and insurance.

Bright offices in King Street opposite Marks and Spencer. Not primarily a bookshop though they do have a small hard-backed selection of guides, atlases and holiday route planners. Some of their own publications such as the Book of the Countryside are excellent and not just appendages to the motoring side of things.

SKY BOOKS
119 Shepherd's Bush Road, London W6 7LP.

071-603 5620

Subjects: General secondhand paperbacks.
Hours: Mon - Fri 10.00 - 6.00. Sat 10.00 - 5.00.
Services: Exchange service.

Popular fiction, sci-fi and other general subjects are sold or exchanged secondhand here. Old magazines are also sold.

DILLONS THE BOOKSTORE
Medical School Library,
Charing Cross & Westminster Medical School
The Reynolds Building, St. Dunstan's Road,
London W6 8RF.

081-741 0881

Subjects: Medical texts for under- and post graduates, nursing and related reading.
Hours: Mon - Fri 11.00 - 2.30.
Services: Special orders, mail order, lists, institutional supply, customer accounts, credit cards.

Located in the library of Charing Cross Medical School, Dillons specialises in supplying students, hospital consultants and administrators, and has a strong following of customers from other hospitals and medical schools. Some general books are stocked for those rare moments of students' free time.

RED AND GREEN BOOKS AT RIVERSIDE STUDIOS
Crisp Road, Hammersmith, London W6 9RL.   **081-741 2251**

Subjects: Literature, drama, arts, latest fiction, green politics.
Hours: Tue - Sun 12.00 - 3.00, 4.00 - 8.00.
Services: Special orders, mail order.

The shop is part of the arts complex. As well as books a wide range of cards and art magazines is stocked.

ACADEMY BOOKSHOP
(London Art Bookshop Ltd.)
7/8 Holland Street, London W8 4NA.   **071-937 6996**

Subjects: Fine and applied arts, architecture.
Hours: Mon - Sat 9.30 - 6.00.
Services: Special orders, mail order, catalogue, credit cards.

This company operates two shops in this narrow street off Kensington Church Street. No. 7 specialises in art, design and photography and across on the North side of the road at No. 8 is the shop specialising in architecture.

NOTTING HILL BOOKS LTD.
132 Palace Gardens Terrace, London W8 4RT.   **071-727 5988**

Subjects: Reduced price books (remainders, some review copies, good secondhand.
Hours: Mon - Sat 10.15 - 6.00 (Thu 10.15 - 1.00)

This shop is part way along the one-way system from Notting Hill Gate to Kensington Church Street and is to be recognised by the blue awning and the tables, with secondhand paperbacks, on the pavement. It is a long, narrow shop, well laid out, and its bargains are rather superior with an inclination towards art, literary criticism and history.

HATCHARDS
Barkers Arcade, 63 Kensington High Street,
London W8 5SE.   **071-937 0858**

Subjects: General.
Hours: Mon - Sat 9.30 - 6.00.
Services: Special orders, search service, mail order, catalogue, credit cards, personal accounts.

Another offshoot of the excellent Hatchards. A general range of subjects but particularly good on art, biography, fiction, travel and children's books.

ST PAUL BOOK CENTRE
199 Kensington High Street, London W8 6BA.   **071-937 9591**

Subjects: Religious books.
Hours: Tue - Sat 9.30 - 5.30.
Services: Special orders, mail order, catalogue, church and school supplies, credit cards.

This shop is run by the Daughters of St. Paul, who were founded in 1915 to promote the Christian message through the mass media. It stocks a wide range of Christian literature, mainly Roman Catholic. Books are on the ground floor and audio visual material on the first floor.

EARLY LEARNING CENTRE
225 Kensington High Street, London W8 6SA.   **071-937 0419**

Subjects: Educational books for young children, pre-school books, story books.
Hours: Mon - Sat 9.00 - 6.00.
Services: Credit cards, catalogue, mail order, a play area, discounts for playgroups, and handicapped children from registered groups.

A shop with books for young children up to the age of 8 years. Brightly lit and coloured, with a small unsupervised play area for toddlers while mother or father looks around the books and toys, most of which have a learning function. A very good idea and helpful to slower learning parents who should be able to launch their young J.S. Mill from here.

CHILDREN'S BOOK CENTRE LTD.
237 Kensington High Street, London W8 6SA.   **071-937 7497**

Subjects: Children's books.
Hours: Mon - Sat 9.30 - 6.00.
Services: Special orders, mail order, credit cards.

Children are well thought of south of the Park and here is another good bookshop for them. The book sections are by age group (up to teenage), and there are also ones on sport, crafts, etc. all well sign posted. The projected refit will include an area for children's events such as visits by authors and artists and story telling. There will also be toilet facilities and a baby changing area, welcome additions for both parent and child.

WATERSTONE'S BOOKSELLERS
191-193 Kensington High Street, London W8 6SH.   071-937 8432

Subjects: General.
Hours: Mon - Fri 9.30 - 9.00. Sat 9.30 - 7.00. Sun 11.00 - 6.00.
Services: Special orders, mail order, school and library supply, out-of-print book search, credit cards.

The high standard of both books and decor is continued by Waterstone's in their recently enlarged premises in Kensington High Street, where they have a corner site with three floors devoted to their excellent stock in general subjects. At ground floor level there is plenty of room to browse among fiction, biographies and their travel section. Downstairs one finds more specialist non-fiction subjects and on the first an expensive poetry, drama and art range. The staff in all departments are very knowledgeable and maintain the stock themselves.

S.T.A. TRAVEL
6 Wrights Lane, London W8 6TA.   **071-937 9921**

Subjects: Travel guides.
Hours: Mon - Fri 9.00 - 6.00. Sat 10.00 - 4.00.
Services: Credit cards.

Primarily a travel agency catering for the young independent market, they also sell guides to all the continents. There are lists of their books provided and they will produce any title one is interested in.

D. MELLOR & A.L. BAXTER
121 Kensington Church Street,
London W8 7LP.

071-229 2033
071-221 8822
Fax 071-792 0214

Subjects: Antiquarian, fine bindings, literature, science, medicine, travel, history, medieval manuscripts.
Hours: Mon - Fri 10.00 - 6.30. Sat 10.00 - 4.00.
Services: Mail order, catalogue, credit cards, search service, binding, and book restoration on the premises.

Recently greatly expanded, this excellent antiquarian bookshop occupies two shops on four floors. The less expensive books are in the basement and at ground level the rarer items are found, and it is here that the book restoration is carried out, which adds interest to a visit.

SHERRATT & HUGHES
**235-237 Kensington Church Street,
London W8 7LX.**   **071-229 9444**

Subjects: General, travel, art, English as a foreign language.
Hours: Mon - Fri 9 a.m. - 10.00 p.m. Sat 9.00 - 8.00. Sun 11.00 - 5.00.
Services: Special orders, accounts, books mailed overseas, school supplier, credit cards.

A spacious new bookshop on the corner of Kensington Church Street and Notting Hill Gate. Trading from two floors, it has a wide range of books with fiction, travel, reference and children's books featuring strongly.

TRAILFINDERS
194 Kensington High Street, London W8 7RG.   **071-938 3999**

Subjects: Travel.
Hours: Mon - Sat 10.00 - 6.00.
Services: Mail order, lists, subscriptions to travel magazines, credit cards.

Primarily a travel agency for the independent, long haul traveller, they have a small comprehensive book and map section with an emphasis on Africa and Australia. Certainly a good place for overlanders who require literature about places between London and Australasia.

W.H. SMITH LTD.
**132-136 Kensington High Street
London W8 7RP.**   **071-937 0236**

Subjects: General.
Hours: Mon - Sat 8.30 - 6.00. (Extended trading hours at Christmas).
Services: Special orders.

Recently modernised and sporting the W.H. Smith 'New Look', the basement of this branch is now completely devoted to books with an increase in the range of children's titles. On the ground floor are music, news, stationery, cards and toys. A lift is available on request.

KANOUNE KETAB LTD. (Iranian Bookshop)
2 Kensington Church Walk, London W8 9BL.   **071-937 5087**

Subjects: Iran.
Hours: Mon - Sat 9.30 - 12.30, 1.30 - 6.00.
Services: Mail order, catalogue.

Down this small mews behind Kensington High Street is the Iranian bookshop selling books in the Persian language and in English about Iran. It has a large mail order business.

W10-W12

GRASS ROOTS STOREFRONT
71 Golborne Road, London W10 5NR.   **081-969 0687**

Subjects: Black books specialising in Africa, Asia, America and the Caribbean.
Hours: Mon - Sat 9.30 - 6.30.
Services: Special orders.

Books are in English but they are described as revolutionary literature. This shop is a co-operative with gifts and African crafts taking up the majority of space, but books are available on politics, race relations and Black studies generally.

BOOKS FOR COOKS
(The Cook Book Shop)
4 Blenheim Crescent, London W11 1NN.   **071-221 1992**

Subjects: Cookery — new and secondhand.
Hours: Mon - Sat 9.30 - 6.00.
Services: Special orders, mail order, wants list, educational supply.

This shop is modern, well lit, floored with terra cotta tiles and comprehensive in its range, with some 5,000 titles on cookery usually in stock - everything from apfelstrudel in Aachen to zebra in Zululand!

The long ground floor area incorporates, at the back, a test kitchen below a glass roof. Coffee, cake and lunch are available, cooked from recipes out of new books.

The beautifully furnished and spacious first floor is available for private business lunches or dinners and has a further kitchen. Altogether a very impressive specialist establishment and perhaps one of the best cookery bookshops in the world.

THE TRAVEL BOOKSHOP
13 Blenheim Crescent, London W11 2EE.   **071-229 5260**

Subjects: Travel (new, rare, secondhand).
Hours: Mon - Fri 10.00 - 6.00. Sat 10.00 - 5.00.
Services: Catalogue, wants list, mail order, credit cards.

A unique shop run by Sarah Anderson about 50 yards west of the Portobello Road. It specialises in travel, but 'specialises' doesn't begin to describe the range and interest of her stock. Old, new, hardback, paperback, secondhand, antiquarian, guides, maps, charts, travellers tales, and biographies make up a partial list. The books are arranged by continent and then by country, all hugger mugger, a pedestrian guide next to a monograph from the Hakluyt Society. Be it the exigencies of space or whatever, it is a private opinion that these are the arrangements most loved by the reading and browsing brotherhood. The shop endeavours to have some books on all countries and has all on some.

THE OPEN BOOKSHOP
15 Blenheim Crescent,
London W11 2EE.   **071-243 1284**

Subjects: Esoteric, spiritual traditions, New Age, science.
Hours: Mon - Sat 10.00 - 6.00.
Services: Special orders, credit cards.

This bookshop specialises in esoteric subjects. The stock is comprehensive ('from Astrology to Zen') and includes one or two surprises: a section on science — covering astronomy, biology, mathematics and new physics — and one on chess. Related items also stocked include aromatherapy oils, crystals and tarot cards. Mr. Shape, the owner, is on hand with expert advice and guidance.

ELGIN BOOKS
6 Elgin Crescent,
London W11 2HX.   **071-229 2186**

Subjects: General, children's.
Hours: Tue - Sat 10.00 - 6.00.
Services: Special orders, displays of book reviews from major
                newspapers on a noticeboard.

An attractive shop on two floors, dark green throughout with wooden shelving and a scarlet blind. It is a good general shop, strong on fiction, poetry and children's books. They keep about 13,000 titles overall in stock.

GOLDEN AGE
3 Denbigh Road,
London W11 2SJ.   **071-229 6765**

Subjects: Nineteenth and twentieth century collectables.
Hours: Mon - Fri 10.00 - 5.00. Sat 11.00 - 4.00.
Services: Mail order list, special orders, credit cards.

An attractive new bookshop, two minutes from Portobello Road, specialising in books on a wide range of popular collectables, including toys, dolls, cameras, ephemera, decorative arts etc.

CHRISTIAN BOOKS AND MUSIC
Kensington Temple,
Kensington Park Road,
London W11 3BY.   **071-727 8684**

Subjects: Christian literature.
Hours: Mon - Fri 10.00 - 5.30. Wed 10.00 - 7.00. Sat 10.00 - 4.00.
Services: Special orders.

Down some steps at the Kensington Temple is this small Evangelical Christian bookshop stocking Bibles, commentaries and study aids, together with a range of popular Christian literature in paperback. Also records and cassettes.

MUSIC & VIDEO EXCHANGE
56 Notting Hill Gate,
London W11 3HT.   **071-229 8420**

Subjects: General, secondhand.
Hours: Mon - Sun 10.00 - 8.00.
Services: Books bought.

The book stock here is secondhand, both fiction and non-fiction. They claim never to refuse to buy books, whatever the condition, age, language, subject or quantity, and have an outlet for low price books at their bookstall not far away at 28 Pembridge Road. The shop also sells secondhand music and video equipment, records and music cassettes.

MANDARIN BOOKS LTD.
22 Notting Hill Gate,
London W11 3JE. **071-229 0327**

Subjects: General.
Hours: Mon - Fri 10.00 - 6.30. Sat 10.00 - 6.00.
Services: Special orders.

A good general bookshop but rather cramped. The principle of book arrangement is a little hard to discern, but one can get most non-technical books here and they are good on new titles which have been recently reviewed.

W.H. SMITH LTD.
92 Notting Hill Gate,
London W11 3QB. **071-727 9261**

Subjects: General.
Hours: Mon - Sat 8.30 - 7.00.
Services: Special orders, credit cards.

A first-rate W.H.S. bookshop. The first floor is entirely made over to books, with generous wall shelving and tables scattered around displaying new titles and fast sellers. Most general book buyers will try a Smiths before much else, and in this branch at least their book-buying expectations probably will be met.

BERNARD J. SHAPERO
80 Holland Park Avenue, **071-493 0876**
London W11 3RE. **Fax 071-229 7860**

Subjects: Antiquarian, natural history, travel and voyage, art and architecture, history and literature.
Hours: Mon - Fri 10.00 - 7.00. Sat 10.00 - 5.00.
Services: Catalogues, bookbinding, credit cards.

A spacious shop next to Holland Park tube station with a large and comprehensive stock of antiquarian books. Foreign currency and credit cards may be used when making a purchase. Two catalogues are produced each year plus specialist catalogues. A bookbinding service is also available.

BRITISH ESPERANTO ASSOCIATION (INC.) LTD.
140 Holland Park Avenue,
London W11 4UF.   **071-727 7821**

Subjects: General (in Esperanto).
Hours: Mon - Fri 9.30 - 6.00.
Services: Mail order, catalogue, reference library, journals on
                 subscription, 33% discount off their own publications to
                 schools and libraries.

More like an office than a shop, this is the only exclusively Esperanto bookshop in the country. One is welcome to look around, but unless one has the language, directions will be needed. As well as books, cassettes in Esperanto are sold.

BOOK BARGAINS
14 Shepherd's Bush Market,
London W12 8DQ.   **081-740 0873**

Subjects: Secondhand paperbacks.
Hours: Mon - Fri 10.00 - 5.00. Thu closed.
Services: Exchange service.

This large stall in the centre of the market has been run for over 40 years by the same owner, who will also exchange books.

BUSH BOOKS AND RECORDS
113 Shepherd's Bush Centre,
London W12 8PP.   **081-749 7652**

Subjects: General, Open University stockist.
Hours: Mon - Fri 10.00 - 6.00. Sat 10.00 - 5.30.
Services: Special orders, credit cards.

This is a spacious, two-level, well lit bookshop in a 1970s shopping centre (soon to be refurbished), offering a good general range of titles. Subject headings are exhibited in exemplary manner with paperback fiction, travel and children's books being their largest sections. At one end of the basement is Bush Records, selling mainly classical music on CD and cassette. They also stock cards and stationery. An oasis in Shepherd's Bush, they deserve to do well.

W.H. SMITH LTD.
64 The Broadway, London W13 OSU.   **081-579 3461**

Subjects: General.
Hours: Mon - Sat 9.00 - 6.00.
Services: Special orders, credit cards.

A very generous portion of this large floor branch is given over to the selling of books, which are ranged around on shelves and centre tables.

WALTER RODNEY BOOKSHOP
Bogle — L'Ouverture Publications Ltd.
5 Chignell Place, Ealing, London W13 OTJ.   **081-579 4920**

Subjects: Black studies, Third World literature.
Hours: Mon - Sat 10.00 - 6.00.
Services: Special orders, booklist catalogue, mail order, school supply.

Renamed in 1980 after the murder of Dr. Walter Rodney in Guyana, this shop specialises in the Black world — Africa, the Caribbean, Europe and America.

BASKETTS BOOKSHOPS
201 Uxbridge Road,
West Ealing, London W13 9AA.   **081-567 5356**

Subjects: General.
Hours: Mon - Sat 9.00 - 5.30.
Services: Special orders.

This bookshop has quite a good range of general books in hardback and paperback and stocks Ordnance Survey maps.

DILLONS THE BOOKSTORE
Hammersmith & West London College,
Gliddon Road, London W14 9BL.   **081-741 1688**

Subjects: Academic texts.
Hours: Mon - Thu 10.00 - 4.00. Two evenings per week 5.00 -
               7.00 (variable). Fri, Sat closed.
Services: Special orders, mail order, lists, institutional supply,
               customer accounts, credit cards.

Like Dillons at Ealing College, Dillons at Hammersmith's and West
London College has a clientele consisting mostly of students and
lecturers, although the shop does supply a growing number of
general customers.

NASHRE KETAB
Book Distribution Centre,
157 North End Road, London W14 9NH.   **071-603 6936**

Subject: Persian books.
Hours: Mon - Sat 10.00 - 6.00.
Services: Books bought, search service, international mail order.

A very extensive stock of books, journals, periodicals, magazines
and postcards in Persian along with books in English, French and
German relating to Iran and the Middle East. Typesetting in
Persian, Arabic and English is also available.

FORBIDDEN PLANET LTD.
71 New Oxford Street, London WC1A 1DG.

071-836 4179
071-379 6042

Subjects: Science-fiction, fantasy, horror, comics, film and television material.
Hours: Mon - Fri 10.00 - 7.00. Thu 10.00 - 8.00. Sat 10.00 - 6.00.
Services: Mail order (01-497 2150), catalogue upon request, subscription to magazines.

Here is the shop for science-fiction and comic fans. A huge stock of new and old books and comics, many of which are imports from the United States and not easily obtainable elsewhere. A large selection of imported comics from the United States, Japan and Europe. Horror, science-fiction and related movie merchandise, plus a wide variety of genre-related toys, games, model kits and T-shirts. It has the most varied stock of any shop of its kind.

NIHON TOKEN
23 Museum Street, London WC1A 1JT.

071-580 6511

Subjects: Japanese art, history and culture.
Hours: Mon - Sat 10.00 - 5.00.

Books take second place to Japanese antiques in this shop. There is a small section of new books and the occasional antiquarian bargain.

BLOOMSBURY RARE BOOKS
29 Museum Street, London WC1A 1LH.

071-636 8206

Subjects: General secondhand and antiquarian, art reference.
Hours: Mon - Sat 10.30 - 6.00. Sun 12.30 - 6.00. Public Holidays 12.00 - 3.30.
Services: Mail order, catalogue.

Mr. Page carries a good general stock. His books are quality secondhand and antiquarian on diverse matters — scholarly, literary, historical and travel.

CHECK BOOKS
31 Museum Street, London WC1A 1LH.   **071-637 5862**

Subjects: Antiquarian and out-of-print, foreign and British travel, modern first editions, art, children's, illustrated, general.
Hours: Mon - Sat 10.30 - 6.00. Sun 12.00 - 6.00
Services: Search service; catalogues on modern literature, first editions, art and foreign travel.

A newly fitted, bright shop with a sizeable and well-arranged stock. The books are always in very good condition with unusual as well as classic titles on offer.

BOOKS FROM INDIA (U.K.) LTD.
45, Museum Street, London WC1A 1LR.   **071-405 7226**

Subjects: The Indian subcontinent, new and antiquarian.
Hours: Mon - Fri 10.00 - 5.30. Sat 10.00- 5.00.
Services: Mail order, subject catalogues, all credit cards, institutional supply.

The shop has a stock of books on or from India, Nepal, Pakistan, Bangladesh and Sri Lanka. The stock is multi-lingual and has a back up of audio aids. There are also some British and American titles covering this part of the world. They have their own publishing imprints (Tricolour Books, Homoeopathic Book Service, Asia Publishing House), with titles on the visual arts and cultural subjects. The owner, who hitch-hiked from India many years ago, and his wife, provide knowledgeable and helpful service to help guide one around their vast stock.

THE ATLANTIS BOOKSHOP
49a Museum Street, London WC1A 1LY.   **071-405 2120**

Subjects: Occult, witchcraft, tarot, astrology, alchemy, folklore, spiritualism, psychic phenomena (new and secondhand).
Hours: Mon - Fri 10.00 - 5.30. Thu 10.00 - 8.00. Sat 11.00 - 5.00.

This well established, occult bookshop has recently changed hands and has expanded its sections on spiritualism and psychic phenomena. It continues to sell both new and secondhand books. Tarot cards and crystal balls are on sale for the initiates.

LOUIS W. BONDY
16 Little Russell Street, London WC1A 2HN.   071-405 2733

Subjects: Miniature books, early printed books, early children's books and books on caricature.
Hours: Mon - Fri 10.30 - 6.30. Sat 10.30 - 5.30.
Services: Books bought, valuations

A small, three roomed shop in a side street near the British Museum. Miniature books are Mr. Bondy's speciality; he has written a medium-sized one on the subject. The remainder of the stock is mainly antiquarian with some modern first editions, D.H. Lawrence for instance, and books on the art and history of caricature. There is a large section of books in other European languages.

SKOOB TWO
19 Bury Place, Bloomsbury, London WC1A 2JH.   071-405 0030

Subjects: Secondhand and antiquarian books on esoterica, archaeology, anthropology, travel, Africa, Latin America, the Orient etc.
Hours: Mon - Sat 10.30 - 6.30.
Services: Books bought, 10% discount to full time students and UB40.

Three minutes' walk from Skoob Books Ltd., among the cluster of secondhand bookshops close to the British Museum is Skoob Two. Smaller than the Sicilian Avenue shop, Skoob Two has a completely different range of subjects. Here are eastern and western religions, magic and the occult, archaeology, anthropology and a wide selection of books on foreign parts.

VANBRUGH RARE BOOKS
Opp. The British Museum,
At: Cartographia, Pied Bull Yard,   071-404 0733
Bury Place, London WC1A 2JR.   Fax 071-831 9150

Subjects: Antiquarian, manuscripts, general.
Hours: Mon - Fri 10.00 - 6.00. Sat 11.00 - 4.00.
Services: Catalogues (about 10 per year), mailing list for catalogues.

Established in 1984, Vanbrugh Rare Books stocks antiquarian books, mainly pre-1800, on many subjects, as well as manuscripts, documents, deeds and pamphlets. They issue about ten catalogues each year, the majority of which are general and cover a wide range of study and collecting.

QUEST BOOKSHOP
13 Bury Place, London WC1A 2LE.   **071-405 2309**

Subjects: Religions and philosophies outside the mainstream, alternative medicine.
Hours: Mon - Fri 10.00 - 6.00. Sat 10.00 - 4.00
Services: Special orders, mail order, catalogue.

The shop forms part of the worldwide Theosophical Movement sometimes known as Esoteric Buddhism, and has recently moved to these premises from Great Russell Street. Subject headings range through astrology, psychology, philosophy, metaphysics and the occult, Krishnamurti, Sufism, Taoism and Zen.

SKOOB BOOKS LTD.
15 Sicilian Avenue, Southampton Row,
Holborn, London WC1A 2QH.   **071-404 3063**

Subjects: Secondhand books (academic and general interest) in literature, the humanities, social sciences, scientific and technical fields.
Hours: Mon - Sat 10.30 - 6.30.
Services: Books bought, 10% discount to full time students and UB40.

Just off Bloomsbury Square, near to both London University and the West End, Skoob Books is a very large secondhand bookshop which has been widely acclaimed. They carry a large stock of literature and literary criticism, philosophy and the other humanities, as well as the social sciences and scientific and technical books.

GOLDEN COCKEREL BOOKSHOP
25 Sicilian Avenue,
Southampton Row, London WC1A 2QH.   071-405 7979

Subjects: Academic.
Hours: Mon - Fri 9.30 - 5.30.
Services: Catalogue, institutional supply.

This shop is a front window for the Golden Cockerel Press, Associated University Presses and Cornwall Books but functions as a normal bookshop. The range of subjects covered is impressive with an emphasis on the humanities; the staff most helpful.

THE SWEDENBORG SOCIETY BOOKSHOP
20-21 Bloomsbury Way, London WC1A 2TH.   071-405 7986

Subjects: Swedenborg (new and secondhand).
Hours: Mon - Fri 9.30 - 5.00.
Services: Special orders, mail order, catalogue, reference and lending library.

This attractive shop fronting the Society's premises in Bloomsbury keeps the works of Emanuel Swedenborg in Latin and in English and other translations, as well as books about the man and his ideas. The majority of books displayed are the Society's own publications.

THE BRITISH LIBRARY BOOKSHOP
Grenville Library, The British Library Galleries,   071-323 7735
British Museum, Great Russell Street, London WC1B 3DG.

Subjects: English literature, children's, history, cartography, bibliography, music, printing and book arts, medieval and oriental art.
Hours: Mon - Sat 10.00 - 4.45. Sun 2.00 - 5.45.
Services: Credit cards, international mail order.

An intriguing new bookshop situated at the entrance to the British Library's exhibition galleries, in the Victorian library which houses the collection of Thomas Grenville MP (1755-1846). Carries a good range of stock, including the Library's own publications. Also cards, facsimiles and other paper products relating broadly to the collections on display.

TRIANGLE BOOKSHOP
36 Bedford Square,
London WC1B 3EG.

071-631 1381
Fax 071-436 4373

Subjects: Architecture.
Hours: Mon - Fri 10.00 - 6.00.
Services: Special orders, mail order, catalogues, credit cards.

The Triangle Bookshop is at the bottom of an iron staircase at the Architectural Association. The books are well displayed and their range is broad enough to include related subjects such as interior and landscape design. Facsimile reprints of architectural books are a speciality, and a selection of international journals is available.

FREW MACKENZIE
106 Great Russell Street, London WC1B 3NA.   **071-580 2311**

Subjects: General antiquarian, fine editions, especially of travel, illustrated and English literature.
Hours: Mon - Fri 10.00 - 6.00. Sat 10.00 - 2.00.
Services: Books bought, mail order, catalogue, search service, bookbinding, credit cards.

A large, high quality stock of antiquarian books in the elegant surroundings of Augustus Pugin's former house opposite the Y.W.C.A., two minutes from the British Museum. They also have a small stock of secondhand prints.

THE CINEMA BOOKSHOP
13/14 Great Russell Street, London WC1B 3NH.   **071-637 0206**

Subjects: Cinema.
Hours: Mon - Sat 10.30 - 5.30.
Services: Special orders, mail order.

The small window of this shop catches the eye of the passer-by with glossy, unmounted photographs of film stars. It concentrates on this one subject, the cinema, very thoroughly. At ground floor level are the new books and magazines and in the basement are secondhand books, stored away awaiting a request.

SOUVENIR PRESS LTD.   **071-637 5711/3**
43 Great Russell Street, London WC1B 3PA.   **071-580 9307/8**

Subjects: Academic, children's, maps and guides.
Hours: Mon - Fri 9.30 - 5.30.

A corner shop opposite the British Museum. It is mainly a showroom and offices for the Souvenir Press who publish on sociology, philosophy, psychology, anthropology and literature. There are children's books from other publishers too, displayed in the window, and a good stock of maps and travel guides.

GREAT RUSSELL STREET BOOKS
44 Great Russell Street, London WC1B 3PA.   **071-637 7635**

Subjects: Antiquarian, early books (sixteenth century onwards), nineteenth century bindings, Dickens, travel, children's, manuscript leaves.
Hours: Mon - Sat 10.30 - 5.30. Sun 12.30 - 5.30.
Services: Mail order, credit cards.

A small shop opposite the British Museum with an interesting selection of collectables ranging from thirteenth century illuminated manuscripts through to first editions and sets of Dickens' works in leather and cloth, travel books and children's illustrated books. Also some prints and watercolours.

BOSWELL BOOKS AND PRINTS
1st Floor, 44 Great Russell Street,   **071-580 7200**
London WC1B 3PA.   **Fax 071-637 2156**

Subjects: Japan (antiquarian, secondhand and new).
Hours: Mon - Fri 10.30 - 12.30, 3.00 - 5.00 (or by appointment).
Services: Special orders, credit cards, mail order, Fax.

Together with their large range of books on Japan they display some beautiful Japanese wood block prints.

FINE BOOKS ORIENTAL LTD.   **071-636 6068 (24 hrs)**
46 Great Russell Street, London WC1B 3PA.   **Fax 071-436 6544**

Subjects: Oriental, secondhand and antiquarian.
Hours: Mon - Fri 9.30 - 5.00.
Services: Books bought, mail order, catalogue (occasional).

If you are interested in Asia, from Turkey to Japan, this is the place for you. Its comprehensive rare and secondhand stock is one of the best in London. Though most of the business is mail order it is well laid out to receive the browser. The Japanese section is probably the largest.

ARTHUR PROBSTHAIN
41 Great Russell Street, London WC1B 3PH.   **071-636 1096**

Subjects: Middle and Far East, Africa, Islam.
Hours: Mon - Fri 9.30 - 6.00. Sat 11.00 - 4.00.
Services: Special orders, mail order, subject catalogues, university supply.

For those interested in the Orient and Africa, this is a renowned shop. Inside one is overwhelmed by the quantity of books but customers can quickly find what they want. There is a geographical arrangement of books, one is told, but you probably have to be an orientalist to perceive it.

COLLETS CHINESE GALLERY AND BOOKSHOP
40 Great Russell Street, London WC1B 3PJ.   **071-580 7538**

Subjects: China.
Hours: Mon - Sat 9.45 - 5.45. Gallery 10.30 - 5.30.
Services: Special orders, mail order, subject catalogues, subscriptions to Chinese newspapers and magazines.

The books here cover all things Chinese, from travel to archeology, medicine and dictionaries. The art section is the largest, and actually extends to Japanese and Far Eastern art. Otherwise emphasis tends to be on the humanities. Upstairs is a small gallery selling original Chinese paintings.

THE MUSEUM BOOKSHOP
36 Great Russell Street, London WC1B 3PP.   **071-580 4086**

Subjects: Archeology, classical studies, travel, history, museum
Hours: studies.
Services: Mon - Fri 10.00 - 6.00. Sat 11.00 - 5.00.
Special orders, mail order, occasional lists, library and university supply.

At ground floor level two rooms are converted into one open showroom. The stock is well displayed and labelled clearly. Despite its name and location it is quite a good all round shop with travel sections as well as scholarly ones. Old and new books live side by side on the shelves.

ARTS BIBLIOGRAPHIC
37 Great Russell Street, London WC1B 3PP.   **071-636 5320**

Subjects: Art, design, photography, architecture.
Hours: Mon - Fri 10.00 - 6.00.
Services: Special orders, mail order, bi-monthly catalogue, institutional supply, credit cards.

Entered through a hallway and sidedoor is a spacious, well laid out room with books on fine art, design, photography and architecture. The books are subdivided into sections — sculpture, painting, individual artists and so on — and there is a shelf of catalogues.

GOSH!
39 Great Russell Street, London WC1 3PP.   **071-636 1011**

Subjects: Comics, graphic novels, newspaper strip books.
Hours: Mon - Sat 10.00 - 6.00 (including Bank Holidays), Sunday 1.00 - 6.00.
Services: Selected collections bought, credit cards.

The latest import comics from all the major companies and a large selection of back issues are on the ground floor and are very reasonably priced. Graphic genre from both sides of the Atlantic (including selections from D.C., Titan and many others) are on the lower level, as well as a large selection of newspaper strip compilations. These span the whole of the twentieth century from Windsor McCay's 'Little Nemo' to 'Calvin and Hobbes'. Much of their stock is imported directly from abroad.

BRITISH MUSEUM BOOKSHOP
Great Russell Street, London WC1B 3RA.   **071-323 8587**

Subjects: Ancient Egypt, Greece, Rome, Western Asia, Orient, prints and drawings, medieval, archaeology, children's books on related topics.

Hours: Mon - Sat 10.00 - 4.45. Sun 2.30 - 5.45.
Services: Mail order, lists.

The bookshop is on the left just off the main entrance to the Museum. Its new location has provided extra space which has allowed for expansion of the book stock with greater emphasis on archaeology, history and related travel books. All civilisations and all the disciplines by which we may understand them will almost certainly have a book or a pamphlet somewhere here.

FALKINER FINE PAPERS LTD.
76 Southampton Row, London WC1B 4AR.   **071-831 1151**

Subjects: Calligraphy, bookbinding, papermaking, conservation of works of art on paper, typography.
Hours: Mon - Sat 9.30 - 5.30.
Services: Special orders, library supply, mail order, lists available, credit cards.

A specialised business selling artists' papers and materials which has a relevant book section. They stock books in print from the United Kingdom, Europe and the United States on calligraphy, bookbinding, papermaking, typography and conservation of works of art on paper. Also specialist periodicals.

THE I.T. BOOKSHOP
103-105 Southampton Row, London WC1B 4HH.   **071-436 9761**

Subjects: Third World development, appropriate and alternative technology, environment.
Hours: Mon - Fri 9.30 - 6.00. Sat 11.00 - 6.00.
Services: Mail order, catalogue (posted worldwide, free), customer orders.

The ideas behind this shop are those of the late E.F. Schumacher, of *'Small is Beautiful'* fame. The shop is owned buy the charity Intermediate Technology, which Schumacher founded, hence the name I.T.. Intermediate Technology works to promote self-reliance in developing countries and the shop carries a range of books on agriculture, building, energy, enterprise development, health, water and sanitation, etc. In addition there are books on alternative technologies more relevant for first world situations, as well as some general paperback fiction and an extensive travel and Third World section.

DILLONS THE BOOKSTORE
82 Gower Street, London WC1E 6EQ.   **071-636 1577**

Subjects: Academic, general, secondhand, antiquarian.
Hours: Mon - Fri 9.00 - 7.00. Sat 9.30 - 5.30.
Services: Special orders, mail order, lists, institutional supply, customer accounts, credit cards.

Located in the heart of Bloomsbury, Dillons the Bookstore has become a London landmark since first opening in 1936. After dramatic refurbishment in 1986, the four-storey, neo-gothic building has been expanded to contain five floors of books in over fifty departments. Specialist sections include a music department that sells classical records, cassettes and compact discs and a new Ryman department with stationery supplies and machines for students or businesses.

Dillons in Gower Street is the flagship store of a growing group which now has over forty bookstores in the U.K.'s leading cities. With a reputation that makes it a place to head for when buying books in London, it claims to be "Europe's finest bookstore".

BUILDING BOOKSHOP LTD.
26 Store Street,   **071-637 3151**
London WC1E 7BT.   **Fax 071-636 3628**

Subjects: Construction industry, home improvement.
Hours: Mon - Fri 9.30 - 5.15. Sat 10.00 - 1.00.
Services: Special orders, mail order, catalogue, credit cards.

A modern, open plan shop with two large display windows on the ground floor of the Building Centre in Store Street. Their 2,000 titles represent the largest stock of books in the country for the construction industry and the home improver. All aspects of the construction industry are covered including quantity surveying, law and architecture. About two-thirds of the books are technical, the rest general.

HOUSING CENTRE TRUST BOOKSHOP
33 Alfred Place, London WC1E 7JU.   **071-636 6796**

Subjects: Housing.
Hours: Mon - Fri 9.30 - 5.00.
Services: Special orders, mail order, catalogue & lists, magazine.

The shop is on the sixth floor. All aspects of housing are catered for by books in paper and hardback, including design, architecture, finance and management. Of particular interest is a section on housing for the disabled or elderly. They have a good mailing service and will send a magazine to non-members of the Trust if required; this includes a list of recent publications.

JEWISH MEMORIAL COUNCIL BOOKSHOP
2nd Floor, Woburn House,
Upper Woburn Place, London WC1H 0EP.   **071-387 3081**

Subjects: Judaica in Hebrew and English.
Hours: Mon - Thu 10.00 - 5.30. Fri 10.00 - 2.00 (Winter), 10.00 - 4.00 (Summer). Sun 10.30 - 12.45.
Services: Special orders, mail order, catalogue, discount for students and institutions, credit cards.

You are asked to sign a visitors book as you enter this large, rambling building. The bookshop is on the second floor above the museum. The books are for the community at large, but particularly the Jewish one.

Religious books, biographies and memoirs, philosophy, theology, Israeli and European history, are well displayed and easily accessible. There is a good selection of Hebrew and Yiddish dictionaries. The service is helpful and attentive.

FLINDERS
10 Woburn Walk, London WC1H 0JL.   **071-388 6080**

Subjects: Australiana.
Hours: Mon - Fri 10.00 - 6.00. Sat 10.00 - 5.00
Services: Mail order (catalogue), book search.

This shop carries a full general range of books relating to Australia and has become a mecca for Australians in London. The stock includes titles of recreated legendary characters, episodes from Australia's history, fiction and a children's section.

MARCHMONT BOOKSHOP
39 Burton Street, London WC1H 9AL.   **071-387 7989**

Subjects: General, secondhand, modern first editions, illustrated books.

Hours: Mon - Fri 11.00 - 6.30.
Services: Books bought, mail order, catalogue.

The books are mainly secondhand at reasonable prices, though there are also review copies and a good stock of modern first editions. English literature, humanities, art and theatre are most prominent.

LCL INTERNATIONAL BOOKSELLERS
102-104 Judd Street, London WC1H 9NF.   071-837 0486/7/8

Subjects: Educational, languages.
Hours: Mon - Fri 9.30 - 5.30. Sat 9.30 - 2.00.
Services: Mail order, special orders, audio and/or video material in over one hundred languages.

These educational booksellers and language consultants have expert staff on hand to guide customers, students in particular, through their extensive range of titles in over one hundred languages. The range of dictionaries in foreign languages is impressive and all this polyglot reading matter is backed up by a large range of cassettes. EFL and ESL books constitute about half the stock.

SALVATIONIST PUBLISHING AND SUPPLIES LTD.
117-121 Judd Street, King's Cross,
London WC1H 9NN.   071-387 1656

Subjects: Christian religion.
Hours: Mon - Fri 8.45 - 4.30. Sat 9.00 - 12.30.
Services: Mail order, special orders, credit cards.

An enormous room holds books displayed alphabetically by author, with the majority of editions laid out for easy viewing. There is a large Bible section and the Salvationist's own publications are here.

U.R.C. BOOKSHOP
The United Reformed Church,
86 Tavistock Place, London WC1H 9RT.   071-837 7661

Subjects: Religious, children's.
Hours: Mon - Fri 9.00 - 5.00.
Services: Mail order, church supply.

Within the premises of the United Reformed Church, whose publications they stock, this shop relies more on supplying hymn books, etc. to churches than on passing trade. Well lit, at ground floor level, and with over 7,000 titles on the Christian faith, all denominations.

GAY'S THE WORD
66 Marchmont Street, London WC1N 1AB. **071-278 7654**

Subjects: Lesbian, gay, feminist.
Hours: Mon - Sat 11.00 - 7.00. Sun 2.00 - 6.00.
Services: Special orders, mail order, catalogue, library supply, credit cards.

'London's gay community bookshop', and well abreast of everything published in their field. They publish themselves; 'Gay's the Word Review' carries book reviews as well as news and articles. Tea and coffee are served.

GROWER BOOKS
50 Doughty Street, London WC1N 2LS. **071-405 7134/5**

Subjects: Books of interest to commercial growers and gardeners.
Hours: Mon - Fri 9.00 - 4.30. Closed for lunch 12.00 - 1.00.
Services: Special orders, mail order, catalogue, credit cards.

An office atmosphere, but the public are welcome to call and look at the titles from Grower publications and books from other publishers on glasshouse crops, field vegetables and nursery stock. This must be the place for commercial growers, but amateurs could also benefit from the many titles — from flowers and flower arranging to theories on weed control, books on poisonous plants and their effect in Britain. A wealth of information for gardeners.

ROBERT CONNELLY
The Bookshop, 31/35 Great Ormond Street,
London WC1N 3HZ. **071-430 1394**

Subjects: History of medicine and science, antiquarian, out-of-print, new.
Hours: Mon - Fri 11.00 - 6.00. Weekends by appointment.
Services: Collections bought, catalogues.

Conveniently located near Great Ormond Street Hospital, this bookshop specialises in the history of medicine and science. Ephemera, prints and *objets d'art* are also available.

ODYSSEY
30 Lamb's Conduit Street, London WC1N 3LE.   **071-405 6735**

Subjects: Holistic books.
Hours: Mon - Fri 10.30 - 6.00. Sat 12.30 - 3.30
Services: Special orders, mail order, homoeopathic clinic.

Odyssey, which stocks holistic books for mind, body and spirit, is situated in the heart of Old Bloomsbury just 5 minutes' walk from Holborn or Russell Square tubes. A sunny, light, airy shop with a peaceful atmosphere makes it ideal for quiet, relaxed browsing. There is a wide selection of alternative health and natural healing titles as well as vegetarian cookery, eastern and western philosophies, astrology, psychology and much more. Mail order is available and the owners are very happy to offer help and advice if needed. A new feature is the inclusion of an alternative healing clinic specialising in homoeopathy.

BERNARD STONE
THE TURRET BOOKSHOP
42, Lamb's Conduit Street, London WC1N 3LJ.   **071-405 6058**

Subjects: General, poetry, children's, the work of Ralph Steadman.
Hours: Mon - Sat 10.00 - 6.00.
Services: Special orders, mail order, catalogue, credit cards.

A lifesize model of Sigmund Freud glowers at the customers here — a sculpture by Lyn Kramer made to promote one of the books by Ralph Steadman (the cartoonist) in whose work this shop specialises.

KINGS BOOKSHOP
17a Rugby Street, London WC1N 3QT.   **071-405 4551**

Subjects: General.
Hours: Mon- Fri 10.00 - 5.30.
Services: Special orders.

A large window enables one to comprehend most of the books in this small shop from the street. Their stock is almost entirely paperback, caters for an educated taste in fiction, is strong on children's books and has a selection of biography and travel.

OYEZ STATIONERY LTD.
49 Bedford Row, London WC1R 4LS.   **071-242 7132**

Subjects: Law.
Hours: Mon - Fri 9.00 - 5.15.
Services: Credit cards, special orders.

Mostly red tape here but a small selection of legal books.

VERMILLION BOOKS
57 Red Lion Street, London WC1R 4PD.   **071-242 5822**

Subjects: General.
Hours: Mon - Fri 10.00 - 6.00.
Services: Review copies bought.

Books on a bench on the pavement mark the spot. Their trade is
review copies, hardback and paperback, which they sell at one-third
off the published price. The books are arranged by subject:
literature, history, military history, art, topography, travel and
natural history are their best sections. Helpful service from the
owner at a desk inside the entrance.

H.M.S.O. BOOKS
49 High Holborn, London WC1V 6HB.   **071-873 9090**

Subjects: Government and Parliamentary publications.
Hours: Mon- Fri 8.15 - 5.15. Sat 9.00 - 1.00.
Services: Special orders, mail order from P.O. Box 276, London
               SW8 5DT.

This shop, established in 1786, has the busy atmosphere of a
wholesale business. The rules and regulations of government and
other established bodies can all be obtained here, the whole kept
running by a large and knowledgeable staff. One can get Hansard
hot from the Chamber and also excellent maps and guides to areas
and walks in this country. It stocks the tourist range of O.S. maps.

PIPELINE BOOKSHOP
87 High Holborn, London WC1V 6LS.   **071-242 5454**

Subjects: General, travel.
Hours: Mon - Fri 9.00 - 6.00.
Services: Special orders, credit cards.

The first London retail bookshop of this well run distribution company. The stock is general, catering for an educated public, and the travel section is worth a mention. Their special order service is particularly fast, since they have the stock of their City warehouse to draw on.

PARKS
244 High Holborn,   **071-831 9501**
London WC1V 7DZ.   **Fax 071-405 9412**

Subjects: Accountancy, banking, law, investment, management, marketing.
Hours: Mon - Fri 9.00 - 6.00. Sat 10.00 - 2.00 (10.00 - 5.00 Sep - Nov)
Services: Special orders, mail order, annual stocklist, computing and marketing catalogues.

A well laid out shop covering their chosen field comprehensively, both for students and practitioners. The taxation and investment sections are the best in the country.

BOOKS ETC.
263/265 High Holborn, London WC1V 7EE.   **071-404 0261**

Subjects General.
Hours: Mon - Fri 8.30 - 6.30. Closed Sat.
Services: Special orders, mail orders, credit cards.

A new branch of Books Etc. with large, general stock.

THE LONDON WEATHER CENTRE SHOWROOM
285 High Holborn,   **071-430 5314**
London WC1V 7HX.   **081-866 4311**

Subjects: Meteorology, climatology.
Hours: Mon - Fri 10.00 - 4.00.
Services: Mail order, weather and climate advice.

The only 'Weather shop' in Britain and possibly the world. A large selection of recent books on weather, climate and related topics, plus maps, posters and technical literature. However, they do not take themselves too seriously and also stock a variety of weather-related merchandise items. How about a 'Storm in a teacup' mug or a 'Happiness is a warm front' T-shirt?

JAMES SMITH
138 Gray's Inn Road, London WC1X 8AX.   **071-278 9080**

Subjects: General (new and remaindered), computing.
Hours: Mon - Fri 9.45 - 6.30. (Sat sometimes in winter).
Services: Special orders, search service.

A small, well-lit shop with an individual character. A willing staff will assist in locating or obtaining new or out of print books. Strong on computing.

BRASSEY'S U.K.
24 Gray's Inn Road, London WC1X 8HR.   **071-242 2363**

Subjects: Defence, international relations, military interest.
Hours: Mon - Fri 9.00 - 5.00.
Services: Credit cards.

Located at the Chancery Lane end of Gray's Inn Road, Brassey's U.K. sell their own books within the defence field. Their subject range includes international relations, technology and general military interest. Though this is primarily a publisher's showroom they are happy to sell directly to people who call there.

FOUR PROVINCES BOOKSHOP
244-246 Gray's Inn Road, London WC1X 8JR.   **071-833 3022**

Subjects: Irish culture (new and secondhand).
Hours: Tue - Fri 11.00 - 5.30. Sat 11.00 - 4.30. (Mon phone first).
Services: Special orders, mail order.

Incorporating the Irish Book Centre, this shop in Gray's Inn Road stocks books relating to Ireland. Art, music, travel, children's books in Gaelic, Gaelic language and literature, history and politics, poetry and a large selection of Irish socialist writings.

GEOGRAPHERS
44 Gray's Inn Road, London WC1X 8LR.   **071-242 9246**
                                                  071-405 7322

Subjects: Maps, guides, A-Z publications.
Hours: Mon - Fri 9.00 -5.00.
Services: Mail order.

A small shop specialising in maps, guides, atlases and globes. They are the publishers of the A-Z Guides.

CENTRAL BOOKS LTD.
37 Gray's Inn Road, London WC1X 8PS.   071-242 6166

Subjects: General, left wing politics, sociology, women's movement, secondhand section.

Hours: Mon - Fri 10.00 - 6.00. Sat 10.00 - 5.00.

Services: Special orders, mail order, bookstalls at conferences given discount.

A brightly lit shop in down-at-heel Gray's Inn Road, with a large, clean window display. The books are arranged under subject headings and in alphabetical order. As well as a very broad range of fiction and books on international issues and cultural politics, the shop also sells T-shirts, mugs, badges, cards and posters.

ROBERTSON McCARTA LTD.
122 Kings Cross Road,   071-278 8276
London WC1X 9DS.   Fax 071-837 9788

Subjects: Maps, guides and globes.

Hours: Mon - Fri 9.00 - 5.30. Sat 9.30 - 1.00.

Services: Special orders, mail order, credit cards.

Robertson McCarta are agents for a number of large European map publishers and carry a very extensive stock of European large scale maps which are ideal for walkers, climbers and cyclists. They also publish guide books and have a friendly and knowledgeable staff. They will try to help with any specialist mapping requirements.

WC2

Lincoln's Inn - Aldwych -
Covent Garden - Charing Cross Road - Trafalgar Square

LAW NOTES LENDING LIBRARY LTD.   **071-405 0780**
25/26 Chancery Lane, London WC2A 1NB.   **071-405 6151**

Subjects: Law.
Hours: Mon - Fri 9.30 - 5.00.
Services: Lending library.

This is largely a library for the legal profession and law students but
there is a retail section. Behind a heavy counter are dark shelves of
books which form the library section. The books for sale are kept
downstairs.

THE ECONOMISTS' BOOKSHOP
Clare Market, Portugal Street,
London WC2A 2AB.   **071-405 5531**

Subjects: Social sciences, including economics, politics,
anthropology, Economist publications, Liberty Press,
World Bank publications.
Hours: Mon - Fri 9.30 - 6.00. Wed 10.30 - 6.00.
Services: Catalogues, account facilities, mail order, special orders,
library supply, credit cards.

The Economists' Bookshop, a stone's throw away from the main
entrance to the London School of Economics, is one of Europe's
leading specialist academic and professional booksellers.

While academics debate the latest theories in the aisles and
politicians and business people ponder the alternatives in the 1992
section, visiting students from all over the world gather together
their recommended texts, giving this lively and spacious shop a truly
international atmosphere.

Experienced staff help guide customers through the tens of
thousands of titles continually held in stock, and quarterly
catalogues provide a selection of the most recent and important
titles in the field of economics and related disciplines. A fast and
efficient mail order service for any book currently in print is also
available.

THE ECONOMISTS' BOOKSHOP — SECONDHAND DEPARTMENT
Clare Market,
Portugal Street, London WC2A 2AB.   **071-405 8643**

Subjects: Social sciences including economics, politics, anthropology, general (secondhand, antiquarian, out-of-print, publishers' remainders).
Hours: Mon - Fri 9.30 - 6.00. Wed 10.30 - 6.00.
Services: Account facilities, mail order, catalogues, search service, credit cards.

Accessible through the entrance to the main shop, with every available inch taken up by secondhand, remaindered, out-of-print and antiquarian titles in the social sciences, the Secondhand Department is the perfect place to seek out text book bargains or that rare first edition of Keynes. A catalogue of selected items is published twice every year and the experienced and enthusiastic staff provide a search service free of charge for books which are difficult to obtain.

WILDY & SONS LTD.
Lincoln's Inn Archway,
Carey Street, London WC2A 2JD.   **071-242 5778**

Subjects: Law.
Hours: Mon - Fri 8.45 - 5.15.
Services: Special orders, mail order, valuation, institutional supply, credit cards.

Beautifully situated in the old Archway at Lincoln's Inn. It is a family business owned by W.E. Sinkins whose father kept records in his head. Today there is a filing system with records of law books published from 1500 to the present day.

Established in 1830 this shop is for those who practice law. At ground floor level the books are arranged alphabetically by subject, from Abortion onwards, and up a few stairs is a large room with antiquarian and secondhand books. Here also is an interesting little display of relics found in the building and newspaper cuttings of famous cases like that of Crippen.

BUTTERWORTHS BOOKSHOP
9/12 Bell Yard,
Temple Bar, London WC2A 2LF.   071-831 3799

Subjects: Legal, tax, finance.
Hours: Mon - Fri 9.00 - 5.30.
Services: Special orders, mail order, catalogues, supply to the legal
                profession, subscriptions to some legal magazines, credit
                cards.

A well lit, modern shop in a side road off Fleet Street, next to the
Law Courts. Hard and softbacked books are stocked and, of
course, their own publications are well represented.

CRAFTS OF QUALITY BOOKSHOP
Keeley House, Keeley Street,
London WC2B 4AB.

Subjects: Crafts, textiles, especially embroidery and patchwork,
                design.
Hours: Mon - Fri 10.00 - 6.30. Sat 10.30 - 1.30
Services: Mail order, special order, credit cards.

A bookshop specialising in the crafts with books on textiles,
(especially embroidery and patchwork) design and other crafts
including woodworking.

B.B.C. WORLD SERVICE SHOP
Bush House, Strand, London WC2B 4PH.   071-257 2575

Subjects: B.B.C. publications, media and communications.
Hours: Mon - Fri 10.00 - 6.00. Sat 10.00 - 4.00
Services: International mail order, special orders, credit cards.

The World Service Shop carries the complete range of B.B.C.
products. This includes books, cassettes, compact discs, videos and
language course packs. An extensive range of books on
broadcasting is also stocked. The World Service Shop is the U.K.
showroom for B.B.C. English language courses. Shortwave radio
information is supplied and receivers are on sale.

THE CITY LITERARY BOOKSHOP
22 Stukeley Street,
Drury Lane, London WC2B 5LJ.   071-405 3110

Subjects: Educational, Wales.
Hours: Mon - Fri 11.30 - 7.45.
Services: Special orders.

The bookshop is in the foyer of the City Literary Institute and mainly serves the courses held there. However, people outside the Institute are also welcome. Besides subjects related to the courses, they specialise in Welsh books (in Welsh and about Wales) and also stock academic remainders.

W.H. SMITH LTD.
11 Kingsway, Aldwych, London WC2B 6YA.   071-836 5951

Subjects: General.
Hours: Mon - Fri 9.00 - 5.30.
Services: Special orders, credit cards.

Until the opening of the Holborn branch, this was the WHS flagship in these parts. There is a prominent book section on the ground floor at the back and the shop has an impressive range of monthly and quarterly magazines on display.

YOUTH HOSTELS ASSOCIATION SERVICES LTD.
14 Southampton Street, London WC2E 7HY.   071-836 8541

Subjects: Outdoor activities, travel, maps.
Hours: Mon , Wed - Sat 9.30 - 6.00. Tue 10.00 - 6.00. Thu 9.30
            - 7.00.
Services: Special orders, mail order, occasional catalogues, credit
            cards.

A large area has been given to the book and map department with entry from the shop or from the street. There is a substantial travel section, and most outdoor sports are comprehensively covered, together with ancillary pursuits like bird watching and camping. The shop is open to non-members. The change in the character of Covent Garden has brought this shop to the notice of many more people than formerly. For the budget traveller there are the Y.H.A. handbooks and other publications covering holidays off the beaten track.

AFRICA BOOK CENTRE LTD.
38 King Street,   **071-240 6649**
Covent Garden, London WC2E 8JT.   **Fax 071-379 4035**

Subjects: Africa.
Hours: Mon - Fri 11.00 - 5.30. Sat 11.00 - 5.00.
Services: Special orders, mail order, book lists.

Situated on the first floor of the Africa Centre, this bookshop has a comprehensive stock of new (and a few out-of-print) books and tries to cover all aspects of Africa. The subject range includes art, history, religions, languages, travel, politics, economics, novels, poetry, plays, criticism, music, cookery, children's and education. Maps, magazines, journals, newspapers, cards, T-shirts, badges, cassettes and records are also stocked. Browsers are welcome.

DORLING KINDERSLEY LTD.
9 Henrietta Street,
Covent Garden, London WC2E 8PS.   **071-836 5411**

Subjects: Highly illustrated general adult and children's books.
Hours: Mon - Fri 9.30 - 5.30.
Services: Catalogue.

A publisher and book packager who produce quality illustrated adult and children's non-fiction, reference and gift books. The shop fronts their Covent Garden offices and stocks their own publications on sport, gardening and countryside, food and drink, crafts, DIY and home decoration, pets, health and childcare and photography.

THE PUFFIN BOOKSHOP
1 The Market,
Covent Garden, London WC2E 8RA.   **071-379 6465**

Subjects: Children's.
Hours: Mon - Sat 10.00 - 8.00. (Some Sundays)
Services: Special orders, post-a-book, mailing list, special service for schools, credit cards.

This Aladdin's cave of a shop has three floors stuffed with books for children of all ages from six months to sixteen years. Books from all British publishers are stocked, together with an exciting range of toys, stationery and gifts.

THE PENGUIN BOOKSHOP
10 The Market,
Covent Garden, London WC2E 8RB.   **071-379 7650**

Subjects: General.
Hours: Mon - Sat 10.00 - 8.00.
Services: Special orders, credit cards.

This excellent general bookshop in the central avenue of Covent
Garden has kept much of the form of its market stall forebear, with
stone floors and an iron staircase to the basement. The ground floor
is used exclusively to display new titles, while downstairs the main
stock includes the complete Penguin list as well as other publishers'
titles, paperback and hardback. The sections on the arts, literature,
biography, poetry, drama and humour are outstanding, the staff
knowledgeable and helpful. The shop is frequently the venue of
signing sessions and other author-related events.

SHERRATT & HUGHES
9-13 Garrick Street, London WC2E 9AR.   **071-836 6757**

Subjects: General and children's.
Hours: Mon - Sat 10.00 - 10.00. Sun 11.00 - 6.00.
Services: Special orders, mail order, credit cards.

A very large and attractive general bookshop on two floors whose
extensive stock covers many subjects. There are books in foreign
languages and a large ELT selection, business and computer books,
a huge travel section, a broad range of books on music, dance and
the performing arts and a very wide range of hardback and
paperback fiction and biography.

Part of the ground floor includes the restored dome and pit area
from one of the last remaining cock pits to be used in London.

Next door is the **Sherratt & Hughes' specialist children's shop.** It
is colourful, imaginative and well stocked, with helpful and
experienced staff. There are low tables and chairs for the children
and some toys, including a full-sized rocking horse, for the younger
ones.

PILOT
34 Floral Street,   **071-836 1131**
London WC2E 9DJ.   **Fax 071-836 7847**

Subjects: Tintin.
Hours: Mon - Sat 10.00 - 6.00.
Services: Mail order, information, credit cards.

A small, friendly shop in the heart of Covent Garden that is dedicated to the Belgian cartoon character, Tintin. Always in stock is the complete range of adventure books in English and French (and often an assortment of other languages). This includes modern editions of the first ever book, *'Tintin in the land of the Soviets'* (1929) and *'Tintin et l'alph-art'*. Other books relating to both Herge and Tintin are also available. Besides books, customers may choose from a very large variety of Tintin merchandise, which includes T-shirts, cards, badges etc.

STANFORDS
12-14 Long Acre,   **071-836 1321**
London WC2E 9LP.   **Fax 071-836 0189**

Subjects: Maps, guides, travel, climbing, geological and maritime
                books and charts, globes.
Hours: Mon, Sat 10.00 - 6.00. Tue, Wed, Fri 9.00 - 6.00. Thu
                9.00 - 7.00.
Services: Mail order, credit cards.

The largest map retailers in the world, Stanfords have a reputation second to none for their range of maps, charts, and all types of travel books. From a large scale section of a British Ordnance Survey map through to huge wall maps of the world, with all scales and places in between, Stanfords can supply any map.

The shop is a mecca for travellers with over five thousand touring maps of Britain and Europe, as well as unique specialist maps imported from Africa, Australia, Asia and the Americas. Stanfords also specialises in detailed walking maps for Europe and overseas. There is an enormous stock of worldwide guide books to match, and the special sections on climbing, geology and sailing are probably the best in London.

DILLONS ARTS BOOKSHOP
8 Long Acre, London WC2E 9LH.   **071-836 1359/1341**

Subjects: Art, artists, magazines, performing arts and literature.
Hours: Mon - Sat 9.30 a.m. - 10.00 p.m. Sun 12.00 - 8.00.
Services: Special orders, mail order, customer accounts, credit
                cards.

Dillons Arts Bookshop, part of the Dillons group, is a specialist shop devoted to stocking books associated with the arts, from painting and sculpture to dance. Refitted in 1988, it gives one the impression of being in a gallery with its modern hardwood flooring and minimalistic curved shelving. There is also an impressive slate and steel cash desk.

In a separate department they stock a very wide selection of arts postcards. The range proves very popular with both regular customers and general browsers.

BERTRAM ROTA LTD.
9-11 Langley Court,
Covent Garden, London WC2E 9RX.   **071-836 0723**

Subjects: First editions, antiquarian, private presses, the Great
                War.
Hours: Mon - Fri 9.30 - 5.30.
Services: Mail order, catalogue.

A pleasant shop with bow windows. Rota's have long been a mecca for the collector of modern first editions and their books range in value from £5 to £5,000.

QUINTO
48A Charing Cross Road,   **071-379 7669**
London WC2H OBB.   **Fax 071-836 5977**

Subjects: General secondhand, antiquarian.
Hours: Mon - Sat 9.00 - 10.00. Sun 12.00 - 8.00.
Services: International mail order, books bought in any quantity.

A good secondhand bookshop with conveniently long opening hours. Literature, history and the arts are on the ground floor. A spiral staircase leads to an extensive basement which houses travel, science, social sciences and paperbacks.

S. SOLOSY LTD.
50 Charing Cross Road, London WC2H OBB.   071-836 6313

Subjects: Militaria, aeronautical, maps and guides.
Hours: Mon - Sat 7.00 am - 7.30 pm.
Services: Special orders, magazine subscriptions.

The hours kept give the clue to this being principally a newsagent. The redevelopment in the Charing Cross Road has kept the owner's circumstances cramped but he keeps a few shelves on his specialised subjects.

BOOKS FOR A CHANGE
52 Charing Cross Road, London WC2H OBB.   071-836 2315

Subjects: Peace, ecology, green politics, natural history, Third World development and fiction.
Hours: Mon - Sat 10.00 - 7.00.
Services: Special orders, catalogue, credit cards.

Sponsored by CND, Friends of the Earth, War on Want and the United Nations Association, Books for a Change naturally reflects their pre-occupations: protection of the environment and its resources; green politics, natural history; and disease and hunger in the Third World. Posters, badges and stickers relating are also sold.

CHARING CROSS ROAD BOOKSHOP
56 Charing Cross Road, London WC2H 0BB.   071-836 3697

Subjects: Secondhand, antiquarian, modern first editions.
Hours: Mon - Sun 10.30 - 7.30.
Services: Catalogue.

Books on most general subjects are stocked here and art is a speciality. There is a basement of reasonably priced books starting from 40p.

HENRY PORDES BOOKS LTD.
58-60 Charing Cross Road, London WC2H OBB.   071-836 9031

Subjects: Antiquarian, modern first editions, secondhand and remainders, Judaica, topography, cinema.
Hours: Mon - Sat 10.00 - 7.00.

While other shops have taken flight from this famous book street, Pordes have arrived and quite handsomely too. None of the stock is 'new', but as aficionados know, there is fine grading amongst the rest, and it is all here. Worth mentioning is the section on cinema.

ANY AMOUNT OF BOOKS
62 Charing Cross Road, London WC2H OBB.   **071-240 8140**

Subjects: Secondhand, antiquarian, modern first editions.
Hours: Mon - Sun 10.30 - 7.30.
Services: Catalogue.

An interesting stock of books. Most general subjects are here, and art is a speciality. There is a basement with reasonably priced books starting at 40p. They also specialise in providing books in bulk (leather or cloth bound) for interiors.

COLLETS
64-66 Charing Cross Road, London WC2H OBB.   **071-836 6306**

Subjects: General, fiction, social sciences, travel, reference.
Hours: Mon - Fri 10.00 - 6.30. Sat 10.00 - 6.00.
Services: Mail order, credit cards.

This branch of Collets stocks quality paperback books and a small selection of hardback books. Fiction, travel, reference, philosophy, sociology, politics, feminism and cultural studies are well represented.

SILVER MOON
68 Charing Cross Road, London WC2H OBB.   **071-836 7906**

Subjects: Feminism, women's writing, lesbian books.
Hours: Mon - Sat 10.30 - 6.30.
Services: Special orders, mail order, catalogue, library supply, credit cards.

The stock here is devoted to writings for, about and by women with women's art and music included and feminist books lining the shelves. A friendly and efficient shop which also acts as a meeting place and information exchange. It claims to hold the widest and best collection of writing by or about women in the U.K.. There is easy access for the disabled.

SHIPLEY
Specialist Art Booksellers,
70 Charing Cross Road, London WC2H OBB.   **071-836 4872**

Subjects: Visual arts, new and secondhand.
Hours: Mon - Sat 10.00 - 6.00.
Services: Special orders, search service, international mail order, catalogue, library supply, credit cards.

Moved from Floral Street to the Charing Cross Road, Ian Shipley specialises in the visual arts, which extends to books on the medium of advertising, including photography and fashion. A specialist shop with art, architecture, typography, graphics, aesthetics and interior design, Japan and the Orient, and their excellent stock of exhibition catalogues, some costing as much as £20. Plenty of helpful expertise here for consultancies and individuals who wish to buy reference books.

AL HODA
76-78 Charing Cross Road, London WC2H OBB. 071-240 8381/2

Subjects: Islam, the Moslem world.
Hours: Mon - Sat 9.30 - 6.00.
Services: Special orders, mail order, catalogue, institutional supply, credit cards.

A three-roomed bookshop segregated into English, Arabic, Persian and Urdu. A wide range of subjects is covered — art, architecture, medicine, politics, Third World — there is a comprehensive educational section backed by records and cassettes, and a section of children's books on Islam in English and other languages.

ZWEMMERS OXFORD UNIVERSITY PRESS BOOKSHOP
72 Charing Cross Road, London WC2H OBE.   **071-240 1559**

Subjects: O.U.P. publications.
Hours: Mon - Fri 9.30 - 6.00. Sat 10.00 - 6.00.
Services: Mail order, catalogues.

This is a shop window for one of the world's leading publishing houses. The books are mainly academic and educational, and it is of course a good place to buy a dictionary. They are also strong on children's books and classic fiction in paperback.

A. ZWEMMER LTD.
80 Charing Cross Road, London WC2H OBE.   **071-836 4710**

Subjects: Photography, cinema, graphic design.
Hours: Mon - Fri 9.30 - 6.00. Sat 10.00 - 6.00.
Services: Special orders, mail order, lists, credit cards.

Since the art and architecture sections have moved across the road, this branch of Zwemmers has more room for its excellent stock of books on films, photography and graphics. The sections are clearly marked and they have some reduced books in their specialist subjects.

LOVEJOYS
(Winart Publications Ltd.)
99A Charing Cross Road, London WC2H ODP.   **071-437 1988**

Subjects: General remainders, full-price paperbacks.
Hours: Mon - Sat 10.00 - 10.30.

A respectable shop selling quality remainders and a good range of new titles and bestsellers, maps and guides, but with a warning to customers as it has a sex shop downstairs.

WATERSTONE'S BOOKSELLERS
121-125 Charing Cross Road,
London WC2H OEA.   **071-434 4291/2**

Subjects: General.
Hours: Mon - Fri 9.30 - 7.30. Sat 10.30 - 7.00.
Services: Special orders, mail order, school and library supply, out-of-print book search, credit cards.

Selling books to Londoners in the evening is the basis of the Waterstone's group of bookshops, with the one in Charing Cross Road next to Foyles as one of the main and longest-established branches.

Now extensively refurbished, this well-organised shop trades from five floors and has strong sections in fiction, travel, history and art. The shop also caters to the academic market and is particularly well stocked in philosophy, computer science, psychology and business, with seasonal students' needs supported. The staff appear to delight in their work and a professional atmosphere prevails.

Advertised regularly in the local press are the very popular author readings that this branch specialises in, which are free of charge and open to all.

W. & G. FOYLE LTD.
113-119 Charing Cross Road, London WC2H OEB. 071-437 5660

Subjects: General, academic, antiquarian.
Hours: Mon - Sat 9.00 - 6.00. Thu 9.00 - 7.00.
Services: Special orders, international mail order, credit cards.

Probably the world's largest bookshop, Foyles, with a little patience on the customer's part, will locate any book he or she wants. It would be a cartographer's task to delineate the labyrinthine departments and to list all their sections. It is best to stalk one's quarry rather than take it at a rush; the stock is so comprehensive that individual members of the staff can sometimes be only marginally less baffled than the customer. The several floors are linked by escalators, a stone staircase and a caged lift of some antiquity. Always a busy and bustling shop, one tranquil spot is the antiquarian department where there is a good range of books and also a section of fine bindings. The remarkable Foyle family line has decidedly not thinned out with the current owner, Christina, whose running of this aircraft carrier of a shop is formidable and effective.

THE BOOK INN/FANTASY INN
17 Charing Cross Road,
London WC2H OEP.

071-839 2712
Fax 071-321 0376

Subjects: General, science fiction, fantasy, comics.
Hours: Mon - Sat 9.30 - 11.00. Sun 11.00 - 10.00.
Services: Special orders, mail order, credit cards.

A spacious bookshop on two floors. On the ground floor are books for the general popular taste along with maps and guides for the tourists. In the basement one is confronted by an array of lifesized colourful comic characters (wood cutouts) and will also find a wide range of the latest American and British science fiction and fantasy books and comics.

COLLETS INTERNATIONAL BOOKSHOP
129-131 Charing Cross Road,
London WC2H OEQ.   **071-734 0782/3**

Subjects: General, politics, social sciences, U.S.S.R., Eastern Europe, children's books, records.
Hours: Mon - Fri 10.00 - 6.30. Sat 10.00 - 6.00.
Services: Special orders, mail order, catalogue, library and university supply, magazine subscriptions, credit cards.

This shop in the Charing Cross Road, just North of Waterstones, is the most ambitious of Collets' shops. Opened in 1976, it is housed in an attractive brick building with plenty of space inside, and now incorporates Collets London Bookshop and its stock on politics and the social sciences. It is also an excellent general bookshop. The specialist Russian and Slavonic section keeps books in English, Russian and other languages, and there is a (mainly classical) record section. The staff are trained and knowledgeable.

NATIONAL PORTRAIT GALLERY
2 St. Martin's Place, London WC2H OHE. 071-930 1552, Ext 23

Subjects: Gallery publications, history, biography, literature, the
Hours: arts.
Services: Mon - Fri 10.00 - 5.00. Sat 10.00 - 6.00. Sun 2.00 - 6.00. Mail order, catalogue.

The Gallery Bookshop stocks all Gallery publications as well as a wide range of books on history, biography, literature and the arts, including photography. The Publications Department produces exhibition catalogues, guides, books related to the collection and on portraiture in general, as well as calendars, postcards, slides and posters. Lists of postcards, posters and slides are available on request.

SPORTSPAGES
Caxton Walk, 94-96 Charing Cross Road,   071-240 9604
London WC2H 0JG.   Fax 071-836 0104

Subjects: Sports.
Hours: Mon - Sat 9.30 - 7.00.
Services: Special orders, mail order, credit cards.

This specialist sports bookshop is located in a pedestrian mall just off the Charing Cross Road, about 50 yards north of Cambridge Circus on the east side.

All sports are represented from cricket, football and golf to fishing, walking and climbing. Since many of the titles stocked are imported from other English speaking countries, coverage extends to such things as Australian rules football, baseball and American football. U.S. sports are particularly well covered.

Other sections cover sports science, coaching, exercise and conditioning, sports medicine, nutrition for sport and the history, politics and sociology of sport. A television set in the shop keeps the customers in touch with current sporting events or shows sports videos (also sold), and a blackboard records latest results.

BOOKS ETC.
120 Charing Cross Road, London WC2H OJR.   071-379 6938

Subjects: General.
Hours: Mon - Sat 9.30 - 8.00.
Services: Special orders, international mail order, credit cards.

A large, relaxed and informal shop, this main branch of Books Etc. is strong on paperback fiction, biography and art, with cinema, travel, and computing also well covered. In fact they have a very comprehensive stock in all general subjects and clear headings and sub-sections to guide the customers to the exact point of interest. Their travel department is extensive, including maps and guides. Certainly a place to visit while in this area of many famous bookshops with easier access to the various departments than many others.

BOOK BARGAINS OF OXFORD LTD
138-140 Charing Cross Road, London WC2H 0LB. 071-836 8391

Subjects. General.
Hours: Mon - Sat 10.00 - 10.00.
Services: Special orders, mail order, catalogue, 10-20% discount on purchases over £50, credit cards.

Specialises in a wide range of remaindered and end-of-line books at 50% or more off the publisher's recommended price. Many books are, in fact, much less than half the price. They will also order a range of full-priced books on request and offer a mail order service with a free colour catalogue for out-of-town/overseas customers.

THE BOOKSMITH
148 Charing Cross Road, London WC2H OLB.   071-836 3032

Subjects: General, bargain books.
Hours: Mon - Sat 9.30 - 8.00.

At the Tottenham Court Road end of Charing Cross Road, this is one of a number of shops in the chain. It stocks best selling paperbacks and hardback remainders and bargains.

THE PHOTOGRAPHERS GALLERY
5 & 8 Great Newport Street, London WC2H 7HY. 071-831 1772

Subjects: Photography.
Hours: Tue - Sat 11.00 - 7.00. Mon closed.
Services: Mail order, catalogue, credit cards.

This specialist shop within the gallery has new, out of print and rare books on photography, technical as well as artistic angles.

FRANCIS EDWARDS
13 Great Newport Street, Charing Cross Road,   071-379 7669
London WC2H 7JA.   Fax 071-836 5977

Subjects: Antiquarian and fine books in all subjects.
Hours: Mon - Sat 9.30 - 7.00.
Services: Books bought, mail order, catalogue.

An attractive, recently refurbished fine booksellers with a well-organised stock and friendly atmosphere. Catalogues are produced quarterly.

GUANGHWA COMPANY LTD.
7-9 Newport Place, London WC2H 7JR.   **071-437 3737**

Subjects: China.
Hours: Mon - Sat 10.30 - 7.00. Sun 11.00 - 7.00.
Services: Special orders, mail order, catalogue, library and institutional supply, subscriptions to Chinese and Hong Kong Magazines.

This shop has a large booklined room devoted to books on China, with texts in the Chinese languages and language learning aids such as cassettes and records. The shop is in the heart of London's Chinatown and serves as a sort of cultural centre. Besides the books, which range from children's to scholarly texts, they also sell attractive prints and artifacts from China.

RAY'S JAZZ SHOP
180 Shaftesbury Avenue, London WC2H 8JS.   **071-240 3969**

Subjects: Jazz, new and secondhand.
Hours: Mon - Sat 10.00 - 6.30.
Services: Mail order, credit cards, discount system for cheques and cash.

Primarily for the aural senses — records, tapes and cassettes, the shop does have some jazz books but only the secondhand ones are accessible. The new ones are kept behind the counter, but the helpful staff are happy to show them to you. Magazines on jazz are also stocked.

ZENO
6 Denmark Street, London WC2H 8LP.   **071-836 2522**

Subjects: Classical and modern Greece, Balkans, Middle East.
Hours: Mon - Fri 9.30 - 6.00. Sat 9.30 - 5.00.
Services: Special orders, mail order, catalogue, library supply, magazine subscriptions.

They have a large selection of books, new, secondhand and rare, on Greece and the Hellenic World from about 350 BC. There are two rooms crammed with stock, and the shop is a centre for the Greek community resident and passing through London.

PARADISE ALLEY
23 Denmark Place, London WC2H 8NL.   **071-836 7148**

Subjects: American and British comics, books, and magazines on fantasy, science fiction, TV and film.
Hours: Mon - Sat 10.00 - 6.00.
Services: Books bought.

Comic back issues and collectable memorabilia are the speciality here. Books and other items such as toys are also purchased, Denmark Place is off Denmark Street.

MURDER ONE
23 Denmark Street, London WC2H 8NN.   **071-497 2119**

Subjects: Crime and mystery fiction, true crime.
Hours: Mon - Sat 10.00 - 6.00. Thu 10.00 - 7.00.
Services: Mail order, catalogue, wants list, credit cards.

Here is a bookshop specialising in crime and mystery fiction and true crime. It has a very wide range of English language titles as well as secondhand and Sherlockiana sections and a special remainder table. A lifesize wax model of Sherlock Holmes surveys the scene.

THE ART BOOK COMPANY
18 Endell Street,
Covent Garden, London WC2H 9BD.   **071-836 7907**

Subjects: Art, design, graphics.
Hours: Mon - Fri 9.30 - 5.30.
Services: Special orders, mail order, catalogue, institutional supply.

Having to ring a bell rather indicates that mail order is the chief method of selling here. Rather office-like atmosphere but books are well arranged and lit, and customers are welcome to inspect. Books on design and graphics, new and old, are their speciality.

THE ALBANIAN SHOP
3 Betterton Street, London WC2H 9BP.   **071-836 0976**

Subjects: Albania.
Hours: Mon - Fri 12.00 - 6.00. Sat 3.00 - 6.00.
Services: Special orders, mail order.

This is also known as the Gramophone Exchange so there are many thousands of records with handicrafts from Albania also prominent. There is a selection of paperbacks and a stock of books related to Albania. Music, travel, and poetry are popular. Titles are mostly in English although books in Albanian are available here. Art, archaeology and current affairs of that country are among the subjects stocked. The shop will be moving from these premises early in 1990.

MYSTERIES LTD.
9/11 Monmouth Street, London WC2H 9DA.   **071-240 3688**

Subjects: Psychic, paranormal, esoteric.
Hours: Mon - Sat 10.00 - 6.00.
Services: Special orders, mail order (lists), psychic readings, credit cards.

All the paraphernalia and metaphysical research equipment is on sale here with an excellent range of books on all associated subjects. Psychic readings are available by resident clairvoyants. The books are well organised in shelves to enable the customer to browse without obstruction from the many oils, candles, jewellery, crystal balls, music tapes, etc.

THE DOVER BOOKSHOP
18 Earlham Street, London WC2H 9LN.   **071-836 2111**

Subjects: Graphic design, fine arts, mathematics, science, music, needlework.
Hours: Mon - Sat 10.00 - 6.00.
Services: International mail order, catalogue, special orders, credit cards.

This intriguing bookshop stocks a wide range of books from Dover, the New York publishers. Their stock includes many reprints of old texts, "Paper doll" and "Cut and assemble" books, Dover postcards and posters. An unusual and completely different selection of books. The staff are helpful and welcoming.

BOUTLE & KING
Pitch 13/14, Earlham Street Market, London WC2H 9LW.

Subjects: General, secondhand and antiquarian.
Hours: Mon - Fri 8.00 - 4.00
Services: Book search, books bought.

An open-air market stall selling hardback and paperback books with a number of antiquarian books always on offer. The range is wide with hardback non-fiction in the ascendancy and some specialisation in theatre and film. The staff are friendly and helpful.

A. ZWEMMER LTD.
24 Litchfield Street, London WC2H 9NJ.   **071-379 7886**

Subjects: New and out-of-print fine and decorative arts and architecture.
Hours: Mon - Fri 9.30 - 6.00. Sat 10.00 - 6.00.
Services: Special orders, mail order, credit cards.

Zwemmer are well known throughout the art world for their extensive stock of new and out-of-print books on all areas of the visual arts and architecture. They produce regular catalogues of new and forthcoming titles, and occasional specialist catalogues. Their staff are friendly and well-informed. The shop at 80 Charing Cross Road stocks titles on photography, cinema and graphic design, while Zwemmer at Whitechapel Art Gallery specialises in twentieth century art and architecture.

ZWEMMER/O.U.P. MUSIC AND BOOKS
26 Litchfield Street, London WC2H 9NJ.   **071-379 7886**

Subjects: Music books, sheet music, scores.
Hours: Mon - Fri 9.30 - 6.00. Sat 10.00 - 6.00.
Services: Special orders, mail order, credit cards.

Zwemmer's newest shop specialises in music and has a comprehensive stock of classical music and books. Not only does it stock the complete range of Oxford University Press music publications, but also a full selection of music and books from Novello, Faber and all other music publishers. It has a wide range of books on jazz and popular music. The staff are helpful and well informed.

COMIC SHOWCASE
76 Neal Street, London WC2H 9PA.   **071-240 3664**

Subjects: Comics (vintage and new), graphic albums, comic strip
             compilations.
Hours: Mon - Sat 10.00 - 6.00. Thu 10.00 - 7.00. Sun 12.00 -
Services: 5.00.
             Wants list, credit cards.

American comics and comic albums can be easily viewed here with
the emphasis on science fiction and fantasy and related
paraphernalia. French graphic novels in original and translation may
be found with other Continental ones in translation only.

PIPELINE BOOKSHOP
37 Neal Street, London WC2H 9PR.   **071-240 3319**

Subjects: General.
Hours: Mon - Fri 10.00 - 7.30. Sat 10.00 - 6.00. Sun 12.00 - 5.00.
Services: Special orders, credit cards.

Here we have a good general bookshop with clear lines, brightly lit
and with a good range of books. There is a wide selection of fiction,
an extensive gay section, and travel, psychology and women's non-
fiction are well represented.

NEAL STREET EAST
5 Neal Street, London WC2H 9PU.   **071-240 0135/6**

Subjects: Eastern, ethnic, primitive and developing cultures.
Hours: Mon - Sat 10.00 - 7.00. (Sundays in December).
Services: Special orders, credit cards.

Besides its traditional focus on China and Japan, the bookshop has
greatly expanded to include cultures worldwide from Aboriginal to
American Indian. Philosophy, literature, travel, cookery, design,
calligraphy, health, and martial arts are all represented within this
scope.

MOTOR BOOKS
33, 34 & 36 St. Martins Court,   071-836 5376/6782/3800
London WC2N 4AL.   Fax 071-497 2539

Subjects: Motor cars, motor cycles, railways, aviation, military.
Hours: Mon - Fri 9.30 - 5.30. Thu 9.30 - 7.00. Sat 10.30 - 5.30.
Services: Special orders, mail order, subscriptions to motor magazines, credit cards.

Two shops in St. Martins Court. Number 33 has the motor books including workshop manuals normally obtainable only from dealers, and in the basement there is a railway section. At number 36 they have the military, naval and aviation sections. The stock is international and very comprehensive, and most is in hardback as it tends to be in specialist fields.

THE ST. MARTIN'S LANE BOOKSHOP
36a St. Martin's Lane, London WC2N 4ER.   071-836 5110

Subjects: General, bargain books.
Hours: Mon - Sat 10.30 - 8.00.
Services: Mail order, catalogue, credit cards.

A smart shop, well laid out and organised, with a pleasant atmosphere. Apart from full-priced, best selling paperbacks the stock is remainders, the cheaper paperbacks being downstairs.

THE COLISEUM SHOP
English National Opera,
31 St. Martin's Lane, London WC2N 4ES.   071-240 0270

Subjects: Opera.
Hours: Mon - Sat 10.00 - 7.30.
Services: Mail order.

The Coliseum Shop, London's only specialist opera shop, has a wide range of books and libretti on the subject. The shop also stocks opera on video and audio recordings together with an exciting selection of English National Opera merchandise.

STAGE DOOR PRINTS
1 Cecil Court, London WCN 4EZ.   **071-240 1683**

Subjects: Ballet, opera, theatre.
Hours: Mon - Fri 11.00 - 6.00. Sat 11.30 - 6.00.

A small shop specialising in ballet, opera, the theatre and performing arts, with prints, photographs and programmes as well as the books. It also sells antique prints on all subjects, maps, signed photographs, ephemera with the emphasis on Victorian valentines, and small antiques. It makes an interesting addition to the very special atmosphere of Cecil Court.

HAROLD T. STOREY
3 Cecil Court, London WC2N 4EZ.   **071-836 3777**

Subjects: General, antiquarian and secondhand.
Hours: Mon - Sat 10.00 - 6.00.
Services: Credit cards.

At first glance you may feel this shop is only dealing in prints but inside they do have a wall of books, concentrating on fine bindings rather than any particular subjects. There is also a small room containing rare antiquarian books.

DANCE BOOKS LTD.
9 Cecil Court, London WC2N 4EZ.   **071-836 2314**

Subjects: Dance, ballet, human movement, folk and ballroom (new and secondhand, out of print).
Hours: Mon - Sat 11.00 - 7.00.
Services: Special orders, mail order, catalogue, subscriptions to dance magazines, records for ballet class, credit cards.

Photographs and posters in the window proclaim their speciality. Ballet to ballroom is covered and the shop is ideally located in the heart of theatreland. Run by the owners who are dedicated to the dancing world and publish their own books, they stock all books currently published in this country on dancing, plus a good selection of American material and a sprinkling of Continental. A central table holds files of unframed glossy photographs of famous dancers — a marvellous shop for the dance fanatic.

PLEASURE OF PAST TIMES
11 Cecil Court, London WC2N 4EZ.   **071-836 1142**

Subjects: Performing arts (all aspects of theatre including music hall; conjuring; circus), Victorian and Edwardian children's books.
Hours: Mon - Fri 11.00 - 2.30, 3.30 - 5.45. Sat (1st in month) 11.00 - 2.00.
Services: Hire for film and TV studios.

A marvellous place to see; full of early children's books, valentines, old postcards and playbills. All the thrills and chills of Victorian ephemera are here. Besides children's books there are many out of print works on the world of entertainment — the theatre, conjuring, etc. Mr. Drummond, the owner, started his collection as a hobby when he was on the stage and has made this charming byway very much his own.

FRANCIS EDWARDS
13 Cecil Court,   **071-240 4406**
London WC2N 4EZ.   **Fax 071-240 8058**

Subjects: Antiquarian and fine books on travel and topography.
Hours: Mon - Sat 9.00 - 6.00.
Services: Books bought, mail order, catalogue.

Sharing refurbished premises with specialist antiquarian mapsellers Tooley Adams, this is the new travel and topography department of Francis Edwards' shop in Great Newport Street.

TRAVIS & EMERY
17 Cecil Court, London WC2N 4EZ.   **071-240 2129**

Subjects: Music.
Hours: Mon - Fri 10.00 - 6.00. Sat 10.00 - 1.00.
Services: Special orders, mail order, catalogue.

The owner has unquestionable expertise on books and music. The shop is much visited by famous musicians. New and secondhand books line the walls and the antiquarian ones are kept under lock and key at the back for security. There is a large basement for stock which can be produced on enquiry. Again a special shop adding to the atmosphere of Cecil Court.

THE TRAVELLERS' BOOKSHOP
25 Cecil Court, London WC2N 4EZ.   **071-836 9132**

Subjects: Modern and antiquarian travel guides and literature.
Hours: Mon - Fri 10.00 - 6.30. Sat 11.00 - 6.30.
Services: International mail order, catalogues, search service, books bought, travel insurance, exhibitions, credit cards.

A beautifully decorated shop on two floors in the heart of the West End, with an extensive selection of modern travel guides and reputedly the largest collection in the world of Baedeker travel guides for sale. Exhibitions of photographs and travel literature are held regularly. The shop is affiliated to Bernard J. Shapero Rare Books of Holland Park.

H.M. FLETCHER
27 Cecil Court, London WC2N 4EZ.   **071-836 2865**

Subjects: General (antiquarian, secondhand).
Hours: Mon - Fri 10.00 - 5.00.

Mr. Fletcher has been in Cecil Court since 1937 and runs this collectors' shop with his family. He keeps a rack of secondhand books outside and inside, has a spacious shop which he is proud to claim avoids subject specialisation but concentrates more on the book itself. The books can range in price from £1 to £20,000.

WATKINS BOOKS LTD.
19-21 Cecil Court, London WC2N 4HB. 071-836 2182/3778/6700

Subjects: Mysticism, occultism, astrology, New Age, oriental philosophy, holistic health, natural therapies, nutrition.
Hours: Mon - Sat 10.00 - 6.00. Wed 10.30 - 6.00.
Services: Special orders, mail order, catalogue.

Initiated at the suggestion of the celebrated Madame Blavatsky and now approaching its centenary of purveying books mystical and occult, Watkins remains a beacon for readers in search of wisdom and inspiration. The Watkins' emphasis is on the esoteric, but their wide-ranging stock includes amongst other things a valuable section on depth psychology. Since their amalgamation with Robert Chris Bookseller, previously of 8 Cecil Court, their subject range has expanded to include practically everything currently available on natural therapies.

BELL, BOOK AND RADMALL
4 Cecil Court, London WC2N 4HE.

071-240 2161
071-836 5888

Subjects: Modern first editions.
Hours: Mon - Fri 10.00 - 5.30.

In its new site Bell, Book and Radmall have maintained their excellence. Very much a collectors' shop, with most of the books classifiable as 'literature'. The books are arranged alphabetically by author, which finally is probably the most sensible thing to do!

THE CLEARING HOUSE
10 Cecil Court, London WC2N 4HE.

Subjects: General bargains. (Most expensive book £1.50).
Hours: Mon - Sun 9.00 a.m. - 11.00 p.m.
Services: Credit cards.

As the name suggests The Clearing House offers many genuine bargains with new stock every day. The after theatre book bazaar!

JOHN ADRIAN
12 Cecil Court, London WC2N 4HE.

071-836 2987

Subjects: General, (secondhand), but especially children's, golf, P.G. Wodehouse.
Hours: Mon - Sun 9.00 a.m. - 11.00 p.m.
Services: Mail order, credit cards, specialised catalogues.

This shop is open when others are shut. There are books in the basement from 50p to £8 and upstairs from £8 upwards. A continually changing stock.

REG AND PHILIP REMINGTON
14 Cecil Court, London WC2N 4HE.

071-836 9771

Subjects: Voyages, travel, natural history (antiquarian and secondhand).
Hours: Mon - Fri 10.00 - 5.00.
Services: Search service.

An ideal situation for a bookshop specialising in antiquarian books on voyages and travel backed by maps and prints.

MARCHPANE
16 Cecil Court, London WC2N 4HE.   **071-836 8661**

Subjects: Collectable children's and illustrated books.
Hours: Mon - Sat 10.00 - 7.00.
Services: Mail order, consultations, credit cards.

Specialising in children's books, this shop is bright, accessible and attractively laid out.

FROGNAL RARE BOOKS
18 Cecil Court,
Charing Cross Road, London WC2N 4HE.   **071-240 2815**

Subjects: History, law, economics, business histories (rare antiquarian).
Hours: Mon - Fri 10.30 - 6.00.
Services: University and library supply, credit cards.

A small premises in Cecil Court with the less expensive items near the door working back to less accessible complete sets, but a ladder is provided for the browser. Lady Finer, who has been in the trade 25 years, gives expert advice to callers.

ANNE CREED BOOKS LTD
22 Cecil Court, London WC2N 4HE.   **071-836 7757**

Subjects: Fine and applied art, illustrated books, bindings, manuscripts (secondhand, antiquarian).
Hours: Mon - Sat 10.00 - 7.00.
Services: Catalogue issued regularly, book search, international mail order, credit cards.

A bright new bookshop just off the Charing Cross Road, which offers a good selection of antiquarian and secondhand art reference and twentieth century illustrated books. There is also a range of nineteenth century fine bindings and a constantly changing exhibition of illuminated manuscript leaves.

ALAN BRETT LTD.
24 Cecil Court, London WC2N 4HE.   **071-836 8222**

Subjects: Antiquarian, topography.
Hours: Mon - Sat 9.00 - 5.30.

A small shop with a gallery to the rear with prints. Old books on topography are stocked together with maps, globes and other ephemera relating to their speciality. There is a large selection of fashion and floral prints and Vanity Fair prints are a speciality.

ADELAIDE BOOK CENTRE
9 Adelaide Street, The Strand,
London WC2N 4HZ.   **071-836 6502**

Subjects: Secondhand academic and general.
Hours: Mon - Sat 12.00 - 8.00. Sun 3.30 - 7.30. (Variable).
Services: Credit cards.

Most of the books are accommodated in the large basement whose walls are hung with prints and watercolours. The social sciences are well represented and there are good sections on philosophy, religion, art and music. Art exhibitions are a special feature. Crystals, minerals and gemstones may be bought on the ground floor.

ST MARTINS BOOKSHOP
The Crypt, St-Martin-in-the-Fields,
Trafalgar Square, London WC2N 4JJ.   **071-839 4342**

Subjects: Modern literature, religion.
Hours: Mon - Sat 11.30 - 7.30.
Services: Church bookstalls, special orders, credit cards.

This attractive and unusual bookshop forms part of the complex in the crypt of St. Martin-in-the-Fields. The shop carries a comprehensive range of psychology and self-help books, Oxford and Penguin classics, modern literature and London travel guides. The range of religious books is extensive, with particular emphasis on Christian spirituality, feminist and liberation theology and inter-faith dialogue. There is an unusual and select range of gifts, cards and religious objects.

JOHN MENZIES (G.B.) LTD.
40 The Strand,   **071-839 6651**
London WC2N 5HZ.   **071-930 0033**

Subjects: General.
Hours: Mon - Fri 8.00 - 7.00. Sat 9.00 - 6.00.
Services: Credit cards, tokens.

One wall of this shop is lined with paperbacks and there are tables of bargain books. Quite good on maps, guides and general reference. Also sells newspapers and magazines. John Menzies is a large chain of stores, shops and bookstalls. This type of shop is useful to office workers in the area and to tourists.

W.H. SMITH LTD.
Charing Cross Mainline Station,
London WC2N 5HS. 071-839 4200

Subjects: General.
Hours: Mon - Sat 8.00 am - 8.30 pm Sun 9.00 am - 6.00 pm.
Services: Credit cards.

Open bookstall accommodating the travellers and selling books, mainly paperbacks, with a good reference section and maps and guides.

AUSTRALIAN GIFT SHOP
Western Australia House,
115 The Strand, London WC2R OAA. 071-836 2292

Subjects: Australia, travel.
Hours: Mon - Fri 9.00 - 5.30. Sat 9.00 - 1.00.
Services: Mail order, issue of $ gift vouchers and book tokens for use in Australia.

Side entrance of Western Australia House, the Strand. All the major Australian publishers are represented and the books are arranged by subject. National, state and city maps are here together with government publications. Besides books there is a wide selection of Australian-made goods for gifts and souvenirs.

HATCHARDS
390 The Strand, 071-379 6264
London WC2R OLT. **(Business section) 071-379 4588**

Subjects: General, business, travel.
Hours: Mon - Fri 9.00 - 6.00. Thu 9.00 - 7.00. Sat 9.00 - 5.30.
Services: Special orders, mail order, catalogue, credit cards.

Now established for over three years, this branch of Hatchards is a well-designed shop on two floors; paperbacks are in the basement and hardbacks on the ground floor. In response to their location and passing trade they have a specialised business section and a good travel section.

STANLEY GIBBONS LTD.
399 The Strand, London WC2R 0LX.   071-836 8444

Subjects: Philatelic (new, antiquarian).
Hours: Mon - Fri 9.00 - 6.00. Sat 10.00 - 4.00.
Services: Books bought, search service, international mail order, credit cards.

This, the "World's largest stamp shop", carries an extensive range of philatelic handbooks and catalogues. Being the headquarters of the company they also hold the full range of Stanley Gibbons Ltd. philatelic products as well as the first general stamp stock available.

TEMPLE BAR BOOKSHOP
1 Essex Street, London WC2R 3HU.   071-379 4609

Subjects: General.
Hours: Mon - Fri 8.30 - 6.00.

Though situated in the Temple, The Temple Bar Bookshop does not sell law books. It does, however, carry a comprehensive range of titles in most subjects. There are two huge book sales in June and November, the exact dates of which may be ascertained by telephoning. Spoken word tapes and greetings cards are also stocked. The staff are friendly and helpful and the patron has been known to frequent the local wine bar in the company of new customers!

Barnet

MUIRS BOOKSHOP
198/200 High Street,   **081-440 8398**
Barnet, Herts., EN5 5SZ.   **Fax 081-441 1101**

Subjects: General.
Hours: Mon - Sat 9.00 - 5.30.
Services: Special orders.

A small, well-stocked general bookshop which has been functioning for seventeen years. One of its main strengths is its book ordering service. It is fully computerised and the staff are friendly and helpful.

W.H. SMITH LTD.
93 High Street, Barnet, Herts., EN5 5UR.   **081-441 7654**

Subjects: General
Hours: Mon 8.30 - 5.30.
Services: Special orders, credit cards.

One of the smaller W.H. Smith branches with books to the right on entering, past the newspapers and magazines. The standard range of general-interest subjects is stocked, including fiction and children's books.

HAMMICK'S BOOKSTORE
2 The Spires, 111 High Street,
Barnet, Herts., EN5 5XY.   **081-449 8229**

Subjects: General, children's.
Hours: Mon - Sat 9.00 - 5.30.
Services: Special orders, credit cards.

A pleasant, friendly bookshop offering approximately 15,000 titles and including a special area for children's books. Other products include maps, greeting cards and talking books. Customer orders are welcomed and many can be supplied within forty-eight hours.

Burnt Oak

THE PAPERBACK BOOK STORE
(Conrich Books),
19 Silkstream Parade, Watling Avenue, Burnt Oak,
Edgware, Middx., HA8 0EL.   **081-959 3365**

Subjects: General, crime, literature.
Hours: Mon - Sat 7.00 - 6.00. Closed Thu and Sun.

Burnt Oak's secondhand bookshop since 1938 was originally a pre-war lending library which operated along the lines of the video libraries of today. It is a small, curiously-shaped shop crammed with paperback books and caters both for collectors and for avid readers. A pleasant place to seek out old favourites.

Edgware

PRIMROSE BOOKSHOP
91 Burnt Oak Broadway, Edgware,
Middx., HA8 5PP.   **081-952 9619**

Subjects: General.
Hours: Mon - sat 9.00 - 5.30.
Services: Special orders, school supply, credit cards.

This bookshop offers a selection of paperback fiction, both light and serious, and books of general interest including alternative medicine, the occult, and sport. There is a business and general reference section and a stock of English literature study texts.

W.H. SMITH LTD
222 Station Road, Edgware, Middx., HA8 7AW.   **081-958 8014**

Subjects: General.
Hours: Mon - Sat 8.30 - 5.30.
Services: Special orders, credit cards.

A general range of books in hardback and paperback including fiction and children's books.

LAWRENCE COHEN BOOKS
297 Hale Lane, Edgware, Middx., HA8 7AX.   **081-958 6677**

Subjects: General, Jewish interest, children's.
Hours: Tue - Sat 9.30 - 5.30. Sun 10.00 - 1.00.

This shop caters primarily for the large Jewish populations of North West London. From the treatise on Jewish Law to the Schlock novel, Lawrence Cohen Books cheerfully attempts to provide the type of book no Jewish home should be without. Goyim (non-Jewish customers) also welcome.

Borough of Bexley

Bexley

DARTFORD HEATH BOOKS
21 Old Bexley Lane, Bexley, Kent, DA5 2BL.   **0322 526155**

Subjects: General secondhand and antiquarian.
Hours: Tue - Sat 1.00 - 6.00.
Services: Catalogues, mainly archaeology, every 2-3 months.

This secondhand bookshop is opposite Bexley Hospital and only a
few hundred yards from the A2. There are usually about four
thousand books in stock but when the market is favourable there
could be another thousand or so on the floor!

Bexleyheath

SHERRATT & HUGHES
75 The Mall, Broadway Shopping Centre,
Bexleyheath, Kent, DA6 7JJ.   **081-301 4411**

Subjects: General.
Hours: Mon - Sat 9.00 - 5.30. Tue 9.30 - 5.30. Thu 9.00 - 9.00.
Services: Special orders, customer accounts, academic, instit-
               utional and business orders, credit cards.

Though comparatively small by Sherratt & Hughes' standards, the
shop spreads over three trading floors. The ground floor features
new titles and paperbacks, including a popular science-
fiction/fantasy section, and is dominated by a wide staircase leading
to the mezzanine. Here domestic and arts subjects are displayed
with handicrafts proving extremely popular. On the second floor the
academic and computing science departments reflect a growing local
demand.

Customers come from many parts of South-East London as well
as West Kent, and local customers find the shop a pleasant refuge
from the Broadway Centre muzak. The shop deals with academic,
institutional and business orders and also individual requests.

W.H. SMITH LTD.
89 The Broadway, Bexleyheath, Kent, DA6 7JN.   **081-301 0802**

Subjects:	General.
Hours:	Mon - Sat 9.00 - 5.30. Thu 9.00 - 9.00.
Services:	Special orders, credit cards.

A generous amount of space is given over to books. There is a substantial range in all general areas including a large selection of paperback fiction and a good children's section. Late opening hours on Thursdays are an added advantage for shoppers here.

Welling

FALCONWOOD TRANSPORT & MILITARY BOOKSHOP
5 Falconwood Parade, The Green,
Welling, Kent, DA16 2PL.   **081-303 8291**

Subjects:	All transport (aviation, motoring, motorcycling, buses, railways, canals, yachting), maritime and military (secondhand).
Hours:	Thu - Sat 9.30 - 5.30. Other times by appointment.
Services:	Mail order worldwide, lists on aviation, military, buses and road transport, search service.

This specialist bookshop deals in secondhand books and periodicals only on transport, and maritime and military subjects. There are at least ten thousand books on show with many more tucked away in odd corners of the building. No yellow lines so parking is easy.

GOOD NEWS CENTRE
Chrissoure, 137 Upper Wickham Lane,
Welling, Kent, DA16 3AL.   **081-855 6144**

Subjects:	Bibles and Christian books.
Hours:	Mon - Sat 9.30 - 12.30. 1.30 - 5.30.
Services:	Credit cards.

This bookshop stocks Christian literature and provides audio visual equipment for churches.

Kenton

W.H. SMITH LTD.
138 Kenton Road, Kenton, Middx., HA3 8AZ.   **081-907 2794**

Subjects: General.
Hours: Mon - Sat 8.30 - 5.30.
Services: Special orders, credit cards.

One of the smaller W.H. Smith stores with a general range of books in stock. Hardback bestsellers and contemporary fiction in paperback are near the front of the shop with most of the other books down the long wall to the right of the entrance.

Borough of Bromley

Beckenham

THE BECKENHAM BOOKSHOP
42 High Street, Beckenham, Kent, BR3 1AY.   **081-650 9744**

Subjects: General, local history.
Hours: Mon - Sat 9.30 - 5.30. Wed 9.30 - 1.00
Services: Special orders, credit cards.

Privately owned by a refugee from publishing with a good knowledge of the book trade and, more importantly, books. There is a comprehensive range of subjects in stock with children's books and cookery a strong point, a good range of paperback fiction and a wide selection of local history books.

W.H. SMITH LTD.
172 Beckenham High Street,
Beckenham, Kent, BR3 1EW.   **081-650 0538**

Subjects: General.
Hours: Mon - Sat 8.30 - 5.30.
Services: Special orders, credit cards.

One of the smaller W.H.S. branches with limited space for books. They operate a newspaper and magazine delivery service which helps to boost the book sales, as customers calling in to settle their accounts often treat themselves to a little light reading material.

Bromley

BOOTS THE CHEMIST
148-154 High Street, Bromley, Kent, BR1 1HD.   **081-464 0231**

Subjects: General.
Hours: Mon - Fri 8.45 - 5.30. Sat 8.45 - 6.00.
Services: Credit cards.

The book department is on the first floor and carries a fairly small range of popular fiction, mainly in paperback, and a selection of general interest books in hardback and paperback. Bestsellers, new titles and bargain books all have a place here.

THE BROMLEY BOOKSHOP
Rear of 39/41 High Street,
Bromley, Kent, BR1 1LE.   **081-313 0242**

Subjects: Secondhand and antiquarian.
Hours: Mon - Sat 10.00 - 5.00.

In a quiet corner off Bromley High Street and only a few minutes'
walk from Bromley South Station. Perhaps a little difficult to locate
first time as the bookshop is down a passageway opposite
Debenham's in the High Street and above an antique shop and
coffee shop. As well as a varied range of secondhand and
antiquarian books they sell old postcards and magazines.

W.H. SMITH LTD.
Bromley South Station Bookshop, Station Approach,
Bromley, Kent, BR1 1LX.   **081-460 1919**

Subjects: General, sale books.
Hours: Mon - Sat 6.00 - 5.30. Sun 6.00 (a.m.) - 9.00 (a.m.)
Services: Credit cards.

The bookstall is in the entrance to Bromley South railway station.
It stocks popular titles in paperback and hardback, mainly fiction
but some non-fiction too. Also magazines, newspapers and
confectionery.

SHERRATT & HUGHES
20-22 Market Square, Bromley, Kent, BR1 1NA.   **081-464 6562**

Subjects: General, academic.
Hours: Mon - Fri 9.00 - 5.30. Sat 9.00 - 6.00.
Services: Special orders, customer accounts, schools supplier, mail
            order, credit cards.

Almost opposite Allders, this is a bright, large bookshop. On the
ground floor there are new titles in hardback and paperback and
large children's and travel sections. Upstairs there is an extensive
academic department which also deals with ordering books for
home and overseas customers.

DILLONS THE BOOKSTORE
7 The Mall, Bromley, Kent, BR1 1TR.   **081-460 3232**

Subjects: General, academic, science fiction, fantasy, bargains.
Hours: Mon - Sat 9.00 - 5.30. Tue 9.30 - 5.30.
Services: Special orders, mail order, customer accounts, credit cards.

Dillons in Bromley is a general bookshop on two floors with a very strong academic content. A library and school supplier, Dillons prides itself on providing organisations with institutional orders. An additional feature of the store is its extensive science fiction, games workshop and TSR sections; certainly the most comprehensive fantasy department in the area.

W.H. SMITH LTD.
132-138 High Street, Bromley, Kent, BR1 3EZ.   **081-464 5044**

Subjects: General.
Hours: Mon - Fri 9.00 - 5.30. Sat 8.30 - 6.00.
Services: Special orders, credit cards.

One of the largest W.H. Smith stores with one of the widest ranges of books found in any W.H. Smith. It is especially good on new titles in both hardback and paperback. The part of the High Street where it is located is accessible only to pedestrians from 10 a.m. to 4 p.m.

Orpington

J. & J. NEWBY
The Book Cellar, 191 Petts Wood Road,
Petts Wood, Orpington, Kent, BR5 1JZ.   **0689 72518**

Subjects: General.
Hours: Mon - Sat 9.45 - 5.30. Wed 9.45 - 1.00.
Services: Special orders, credit cards.

A small but comprehensive general bookshop with helpful and friendly staff. Any book in print can be ordered. Browsers are welcome, especially children.

W.H. SMITH LTD.
189/193 High Street, Orpington, Kent, BR6 0PF.　　　**0689 71516**

Subjects: General.
Hours: Mon - Sat 8.30 - 5.30.
Services: Special orders, credit cards.

This large W.H. Smith is the only store with a book department in Orpington High Street. Consequently, special orders are a strong feature. The book department has a middling-sized stock in comparison with other branches.

Petts Wood

RAINBOW CHRISTIAN CENTRE
87 Queensway, Petts Wood, Kent, BR5 1DQ.　　　**0689 21789**

Subjects:
Hours: Christianity.
Services: Mon - Sat 9.00 - 5.30.

This shop stocks Christian books, cassettes and greeting cards. There are crafts from the Third World and church supplies including candles, wafers and stationery. Office services available are printing of social, church and business stationery and typing.

West Wickham

W.H. SMITH LTD.
39 High Street, West Wickham, Kent, BR4 0LR.　　　**081-776 0306**

Subjects: General.
Hours: Mon - Sat 8.30 - 5.30.
Services: Special orders, credit cards.

As this is West Wickham's only bookshop, it has a comprehensive ordering service. It stocks current bestsellers in paperback and hardback and has a good local interest department. Otherwise a fairly small general range which includes children's books.

Croydon

W.H. SMITH LTD.
East Croydon Station, Station Approach,
Croydon, Surrey, CR0 1LF.   **081-686 1296**

Subjects: General.
Hours: Mon - Fri 6.00 - 6.30. Sat 6.00 - 4.30.
Services: Credit cards.

This shop on the station concourse has a small selection of paperback fiction and some maps and guides. There is a sale table of bargain books.

PAPERBACK PARADE LTD
5 Suffolk House, George Street,
Croydon Surrey, CR0 1PE.   **081-681 2050**

Subjects: General, mass market paperbacks.
Hours: Mon - Sat 9.00 - 5.30.
Services: Paperback orders (24 hours), photo processing, credit cards.

The shop is situated near East Croydon railway station. As the name implies it is a bookshop specialising in paperbacks. There is an extensive range of stock and back stock and a fine selection of quality paperbacks. Bargain books are also available.

PHANTOM ZONE   **081-688 3226**
11 Keeley Road, Croydon, Surrey, CR0 1TF.   **Fax 081-681 0618**

Subjects: Comics.
Hours: Mon - Fri 10.00 - 6.00. Thu 10.00 - 7.00. Sat 9.00 - 6.00.

Since their humble origins in the funny pages, comics have travelled a long way to become a serious and entertaining art form. This colourful shop stocks a whole range of American and European comics as well as associated books on horror, film, TV, back issues and T-shirts. Here the collector and the curious alike may enter a world of fantasy and fun.

VOLUME 1 BOOKSHOP
112 North End, Croydon, Surrey, CR0 1UD.   **081-688 0231**

Subjects: General.
Hours: Mon - Sat 9.00 - 6.00.
Services: Special orders, credit cards.

A general bookshop stocking both paperbacks and hardbacks. There is a comprehensive range of paperback fiction from many of the major publishers, a selection of books on subjects of popular general interest such as cookery, gardening, and travel and a children's section.

W.H. SMITH LTD.
140 Whitgift Centre, Croydon, Surrey, CR0 1US.   **081-681 1249**

Subjects: General.
Hours: Mon - Sat 8.45 - 5.30. Thu 8.45 - 8.00. (8.00 a.m. opening for news only). Extended hours at Christmas.

There are two W.H.Smith stores in the Whitgift Centre, both on the lower level. Only one of them, however, sells books. It is a very spacious shop with a large general range in both hardback and paperback. The children's section has a wooden Thomas the Tank Engine for them to play on which is obviously popular with future engine drivers. It has two carriages which function as bookcases. Most of the shop space is given over to books but there is a newspaper and magazine section and also a travel agency in the same store.

SHERRATT AND HUGHES
1063-1067 Whitgift Centre, Croydon,
Surrey, CR0 1UW.   **081-686 7032**

Subjects: General, academic and student textbooks, Open University courses, children's.
Hours: Mon, Wed, Fri 9.00 - 5.30. Tue 10.00 - 5.30. Thu 9.00 - 8.00. Sat 9.00 - 6.00.
Services: Special orders, school, company and library orders, account facilities for institutional and business customers, credit cards.

A bookbuyer's oasis amongst the concrete tower blocks of Croydon, this is a comprehensive and well stocked bookshop with a range that caters for every taste. As the largest bookshop in South London, this branch of Sherratt & Hughes (previously known as Websters) has a number of specialities including computer books, psychology and social work, business books, science-fiction and fantasy comics. There is a wide selection of daily newspapers and periodicals, and books on tape and language cassettes are also available.

SCRIPTURE UNION BOOKSHOP
16 Park Street, Croydon, Surrey, CR0 1YE.   **081-686 2772**

Subjects: Christian books.
Hours: Mon - Sat 9.00 - 5.30. Wed 9.30 - 5.30.
Services: Special orders, mail order.

Conveniently situated in the shopping centre close to East Croydon station, they provide a comprehensive range of Christian books, records, cassettes, videos and cards. The staff are happy to advise and also enjoy assisting church bookstalls. They offer a speedy special order service on stock lines as well as mail order.

PLUS BOOKS LTD.
341 London Road, West Croydon, CR0 3PA.   **081-684 4651**

Subjects: Secondhand paperbacks and magazines.
Hours: Mon - Sat 9.00 - 6.00.
Services: Book exchange.

A general range of secondhand paperbacks and magazines for purchase or exchange.

DILLONS THE BOOKSTORE
12 High Street, Croydon, Surrey, CR9 1UT.   **081-688 3811**

Subjects: General, academic.
Hours: Mon - Sat 9.00 - 5.30. Tue 9.45 - 5.30.
Services: Special orders, mail order, lists, institutional supply, customer accounts, credit cards.

Croydon's Dillons is located in the town's busy centre. The store stocks an abundance of general books for its size and the popular academic department is currently being expanded owing to demand. A plus for the businesses in the area is Dillons' large stationery department which specialises in office supplies. Travel enthusiasts delight in the specialist travel section which keeps a vast range of local and international maps. Art materials are also stocked.

Purley

W.H. SMITH LTD.
8 Russell Hill Road, Purley, Surrey, CR2 2LA.   **081-668 6966**

Subjects: General.
Hours: Mon - Sat 8.30 - 5.30.
Services: Special orders, credit cards.

A small range of books in the usual general subjects with paperback fiction to the fore.

Southall

VIRDEE BROTHERS
26 South Road, Southall, Middx., UB1 1RR.   **081-571 4870**

Subjects: Fiction in Hindi, Punjabi, Urdu, Gujerati, including children's books.
Hours: Mon - Sun 10.00 - 7.00.
Services: Mail order, credit cards.

This bookshop offers fiction and poetry in four of the many South Asian languages. Children's books and recordings of Indian music are also stocked.

VIRDEE BROTHERS
102 The Green, Southall, Middx., UB2 4BQ.   **081-574 4765**

Subjects: Fiction in Hindi, Punjabi, Urdu, Gujerati, including children's books.
Hours: Mon - Sun 1.00 - 8.00.
Services: Mail order, credit cards.

This business provides a similar service to the one in South Road. Half of the shop is devoted to recordings of music from India and the rest of it functions as a bookshop. It stocks mainly Hindi and Punjabi fiction and poetry and has a smaller selection of books in Urdu and Gujerati. There is a children's section and some educational books for those wishing to learn these languages.

Enfield

GORDON ROAD BOOKSHOP
36 Gordon Road, Enfield, Middx., EN2 0PZ.   **081-366 0722**

Subjects: General, children's (secondhand and antiquarian).
Hours: Tue, Thurs 1.00 - 5.00. Sat 10.30 - 3.30.

A secondhand bookshop stocking a wide range of subjects in both hardback and paperback. There is ample parking at the side and front with no restrictions.

FAGINS BOOKSHOPS PLC
37 Church Street, Enfield, Middx., EN2 6AJ.   **081-363 9319**

Subjects: General.
Hours: Mon - Fri 9.30 - 5.30. Sat 9.00 - 5.30.
Services: Customer orders, post-a-book, school and business supply, mail order, credit cards.

A friendly, lively community bookshop with a good local reputation. Although small, it contains a wide variety of books with children's, travel and computer books strongly featured.

W.H. SMITH LTD.
Palace Gardens Centre, Enfield, Middx., EN2 6SN. 081-366 3633

Subjects: General.
Hours: Mon - Wed 9.00 - 5.30. Thu 9.00 - 8.00. Fri - Sat 8.30 - 6.00.
Services: Post-a-book, special orders, credit cards.

W.H. Smith Enfield is the main bookshop of the town and surrounding area. Not surprisingly therefore, they specialise in an extensive ordering service, credit card bookings and post-a-book service. There is a wide selection of news, stationery and music.

Harrow

W.H. SMITH LTD.
St. Ann's Shopping Centre, St. Ann's Road,
Harrow, Middx., HA1 1AS.   **081-863 9374**

Subjects: General.
Hours: Mon - Sat 9.00 - 6.00. Thu 9.00 - 8.00.
Services: Special orders, credit cards.

A bright, well lit W.H.Smith in the new St. Ann's Shopping Centre.
It is spacious and has a fairly large general range of books.

HAMMICK'S BOOKSTORE
35 St. Ann's Road, Harrow, Middx., HA1 1JU.   **081-863 4578**

Subjects: General, children's.
Hours: Mon - Sat 9.00 - 5.30.
Services: Special orders, credit cards.

A pleasant, friendly bookshop offering approximately 15,000 titles
and including a special area for children's books. Other products
include maps, greetings cards and talking books. Customer orders
are welcomed and many can be supplied within forty-eight hours.

SCRIPTURE UNION BOOKSHOP
11 Masons Avenue, Wealdstone,
Harrow, Middx., HA3 5AH.   **081-861 3259**

Subjects: Christian faith.
Hours: Mon - Sat 9.00 - 5.30.

A large Christian bookshop opposite Harrow and Wealdstone
railway station which is on a direct line from Euston. It is part of
a wider organisation with many shops around the country. A
comprehensive range of Bibles, commentaries and Christian books
is stocked along with compact discs, cassettes and greetings cards.
Their play den is popular with young children and even more so
with their parents. They have been called a haven of peace in a mad
world.

Pinner

CORBETT'S BOOKSHOP (Pinner) LTD.
56 Bridge Street, Pinner, Middx., HA5 3JF.   **081-866 8517**

Subjects: General.
Hours: Mon - Sat 9.15 - 5.15.
Services: Special orders.

Corbett's operate from two shops only a few minutes' brisk walk
apart. This branch has a wide range of titles in both hardback and
paperback. The subject range includes travel and maps, pets, science
fiction, sport, astrology, mystery and crime. Special orders for
customers are a strong feature.

CORBETT'S BOOKSHOP (Pinner) LTD.
102 Marsh Road, Pinner, Middx., HA5 5NA. 081-866 1336/3956

Subjects: Educational.
Hours: Mon - Sat 9.00 - 5.30.
Services: Special orders.

The subjects here are mainly educational and include E.F.L. books,
Open University foundation courses, and poetry and drama study-
aids. Special orders for customers are an important feature.

Romford

HAVERING CHRISTIAN BOOKSHOP AND CENTRE
80 Victoria Road, Romford, Essex, RM1 2LT.   **0708 27625**

Subjects: Christian faith.
Hours: Mon - Sat 9.00 - 5.30.
Services: Video library, video equipment hire, photocopying.

This shop offers a wide selection of biographies and teaching books relating to the Christian faith. Gift items such as pictures are stocked as well as greetings cards for all occasions and a wide selection of Christian music on record, cassette and compact disc. There is a large video library with videos for loan together with the necessary equipment and a tea room at the rear of the shop.

APEX LIBRARIES (1942) LTD.
24 Quadrant Arcade, Market Place,
Romford, Essex, RM1 3ED.   **0708 40952**

Subjects: General paperbacks.
Hours: Mon - Sat 7.00 - 5.30.

The stock of popular fiction here is changed every two months. Other popular general subjects include biography, health and diet, humour, cookery and travel.

W.H. SMITH LTD.
8 The Liberty, Romford, Essex, RM1 3RL.   **0708 762317**

Subjects: General.
Hours: Mon - Thu 8.30 - 5.30. Fri, Sat 8.30 - 5.45.
Services: Special orders, credit cards.

A large, L-shaped W.H.Smith at street level with a very generous area given over to books. There is a sizeable range in all general subjects, fiction and non-fiction, hardback and paperback, with bestsellers and new titles displayed prominently. Newspapers, magazines, stationery, recorded music and greetings cards are also stocked.

Upminster

SWAN LIBRARIES BOOKSHOP
27 Corbets Tey Road, Upminster,
Essex, RM14 2AR.   **04022 22930**

Subjects: General, local history.
Hours: Mon - Thu 9.00 - 5.30. Fri 9.00 - 6.00. Sat 9.00 - 5.30.
Services: Special orders, mail order, school supply, credit cards.

Established over fifty years ago, this comprehensively stocked general bookshop is run by enthusiastic, helpful and experienced staff. Books on militaria, transport and local history feature prominently along with all the categories and services one would expect to find in a well run general bookshop. Browsers are welcome.

Hayes

W.H. SMITH LTD.
6/8 Station Road, Hayes, Middx., UB3 4DA.   **081-848 9884**

Subjects: General.
Hours: Mon - Sat 8.30 - 5.30.
Services: Special orders, credit cards.

A range of books in general subjects including fiction and children's books.

Ickenham

A.F. BIRD
73 Swakeley's Road, Ickenham,
Uxbridge, Middx., UB10 8DD.   **08956 34177**

Subjects: General, children's.
Hours: Mon - Fri 9.00 - 5.30. Wed 9.00 - 5.00. Sat 9.00 - 1.00.

Primarily a stationer's but with a small selection of books at the rear of the shop. General subjects are stocked and there is a children's section with the full range of Ladybird publications.

THE HAYES BOOKSHOP
6 Glebe Avenue, Ickenham,
Uxbridge, Middx., UB10 8PB.   **08956 37725**

Subjects: General, new, secondhand and antiquarian.
Hours: Mon - Sat 9.30 - 5.30. (Closed occasional Mon).
Services: Search service, special orders (new books).

A small, well lit bookshop with a warm and welcoming atmosphere. It is packed with books, with remainders and new books along the right wall on entering and the rest of the space occupied by secondhand books shelved under subject. The proprietor and his wife speak French and Spanish, a great help to Continental visitors who will get a good reception here. There is also a print-framing service.

Northwood

NORTHWOOD BOOKSHOP
46 Green Lane, Northwood, Middx., HA6 2QB. 09274 26999

Subjects: General.
Hours: Mon - Fri 9.15 - 5.30. Wed 9.15 -1.00. Sat 9.00 - 5.30.
Services: Credit cards, book tokens.

This independently owned bookshop offers a fine selection of new books in both hardback and paperback on a wide range of subjects as well as the latest novels and biographies. Accessible by car with the municipal car park nearby, or by underground to Northwood station followed by a three hundred yard walk. Other services offered include photocopying, Fax and picture framing.

Ruislip

W.H. SMITH LTD.
76 High Street, Ruislip, Middx., HA4 7AA. 0895 632108

Subjects: General.
Hours: Mon - Sat 8.30 - 5.30.
Services: Special orders, credit cards.

A long, narrow shop with the books along the right wall as you enter and on two central stands near the entrance. A fairly small range of books in the usual general subjects.

THE BOOK SHOP
51 High Street, Ruislip, Middx., HA4 7BD. 0895 678269

Subjects: General.
Hours: Mon - Fri 9.15 - 5.30. Sat 9.15 - 5.00.
Services: Special orders, schools supplier, credit cards.

The Book Shop at Ruislip is one of five shops spread around the home counties with its Head Office at Princes Risborough. The Ruislip shop offers a sprinkling of general subjects but its main strength lies in the fact that it is prepared to go to great lengths to obtain any book in print. The group started trading in 1979 and takes pride in the quality of its service.

Uxbridge

THOMAS BARNARD
11 Windsor Street, Uxbridge, Middx., UB8 1AB.   **0895 58054**

Subjects: Secondhand books, maps and prints.
Hours: Mon - Sat 9.00 - 5.00. Wed 9.00 - 1.00.
Services: Books bought and sold, picture framing, book binding.

Two minutes' walk from the underground station, the shop is a fine seventeenth century building in the heart of Uxbridge. Retaining its character, the shop has recently been extended to give greater prominence to its range of local maps and prints as well as more room for browsers and the piles of books.

MARANATHA CHRISTIAN BOOKSHOP
22 Windsor Street, Uxbridge, Middx., UB8 1AB.   **0895 55748**

Subjects: Bibles, Christian literature.
Hours: Mon - Sat 9.00 - 5.30.
Services: Mail order, video library, photocopying service, suppliers to book agents, credit cards.

A specialist bookshop providing a wide range of Christian-related material including music books and church supplies. Book sections are clearly labelled and the staff are friendly and helpful. There is also a children's play area and a coffee shop with seating for twenty-four people.

BARNARD'S BOOKSHOP
50 Windsor Street, Uxbridge,
Middx., UB8 1AB.   **0895 32751/34858**

Subjects: General, maps and guides, college texts.
Hours: Mon - Sat 9.00 - 5.30.
Services: Special orders, school and business supply, credit cards.

Across the road from Thomas Barnard, Barnard's Bookshop prides itself in giving the customer a friendly and efficient service. Two floors of this Victorian building contain a large and varied stock. All interests are catered for but particular attention is given to the travel, computing and business sections. The shop also carries a selection of distinctive cards and gift-wrap.

W.H. SMITH LTD.
148 High Street, Uxbridge, Middx., UB8 1JY.　　　**0895 56221**

Subjects: General.
Hours: Mon - Fri 8.30 - 5.30. Sat 8.30 - 6.00.
Services: Special orders, credit cards.

A large W.H.Smith store on two floors with the books and the travel agency at the rear of the store on the ground floor. There is a general range of books in hardback and paperback.

JOHN MENZIES (G.B.) LTD.
2 Mercer Walk, The Pavilions,
Uxbridge, Middx., UB8 1LJ.　　　**0895 30887**

Subjects: Paperbacks, bargain books.
Hours: Mon - Sat 9.00 - 5.30.

Situated in a modernised shopping centre, this branch of John Menzies caters particularly for the leisure reader with their range of paperbacks and magazines. Publishers' remainders at bargain prices are a feature.

BRUNEL UNIVERSITY BOOKSHOP
Brunel University, Cleveland Road,
Uxbridge, Middx, UB8 3PH.　　　**0895 57991**

Subjects: Biology, chemistry, computer science, engineering (electrical and mechanical), government, human science, materials technology, physics, fiction.
Hours: Mon - Fri 9.00 - 5.00.
Services: Account facilities, mail order, special orders, credit cards.

The shop, located near the main entrance to Brunel University and recently acquired by the Economists' Bookshop group, stocks a wide range of recommended student texts as well as a good selection of stationery products. Special orders are happily taken by the helpful and friendly staff.

West Drayton

S.R. WICKS & SON
18 Station Road, West Drayton, Middx, UB7 7BU. 0895 442302

Subjects: General, paperbacks.
Hours: Mon - Fri 7.00 - 5.30. Sat 7.00 - 5.00.
Services: Special orders, credit cards.

This newsagents and office stationers has a book section with quite a wide range of paperbacks covering both fiction and popular general subjects.

Brentford

ALBION SCOTT/CONNOISSEUR MOTOBOOKS
51 York Road,   081-569 3404/5/0595
Brentford, Middx., TW8 0QP.   (Ansaphone) 081-847 0511

Subjects: Motoring, military, aviation, modelling, shipping.
Hours: Mon - Fri 9.00 - 5.30. Sat 9.00 - 4.00.

With the closure of Connoisseur Carbooks' original shop in Chiswick, the showroom at the Brentford headquarters has been stocked and arranged in exactly the same way, providing a virtual replica of the previous shop. Many more books are stocked in the adjoining warehouse, including bargains, technical manuals and books which are out of print. There are other retail outlets at Foyles, 113-119 Charing Cross Road, WC2, and on the first floor of Oppenheim Booksellers, 7/9 Exhibition Road, South Kensington SW7.

Hounslow

W.H. SMITH LTD.
201/205 High Street, Hounslow, Middx., TW3 1BL.081-577 3930

Subjects: General.
Hours: Mon - Sat 9.00 - 6.00.
Services: Special orders, credit cards.

This W.H. Smith store stocks a range of paperbacks and hardbacks in general subjects including fiction and children's books.

BRIDGE CENTRE BOOKSHOP
Holy Trinity Church, High Street,   081-570 4586
Hounslow, Middx., TW3 1HG.   081-577 0388

Subjects: Christian books.
Hours: Mon - Sat 9.30 - 5.00
Services: Sale-or-return and discount to local church book agents, R.E. resource display for teachers, special orders, credit cards.

The bookshop was opened in 1983 when it was built on to Holy Trinity Church. Together with the adjacent coffee shop, the purpose is to bridge the gap between the Church and the High Street, both physically and spiritually. It is owned by a charitable trust which aims to foster the unity and renewal of the church. This aim is reflected in a wide ecumenical range of titles and goods including music tapes and cards.

Isleworth

OPEN BOOKS
West London Institute of Higher Education,
Lancaster House, Borough Road, Isleworth,
Middlesex, TW7 5DU.   **081-891 0121**

Subjects: Course textbooks, history, American studies, general, secondhand.
Hours: Mon - Fri 11.00 - 2.00. 3.00 - 4.30. Termtime only.

A campus bookshop catering for the students at the Institute but also open to the public.

CHATER & SCOTT LTD.
8 South Street, Isleworth, Middx., TW7 7BG.   **081-568 9750**

Subjects: Motoring, motorcycling, new, secondhand, out-of-print.
Hours: Mon - Sat 9.00 - 5.30.
Services: Mail order, special orders, catalogue, books bought, credit cards.

A friendly shop which has specialised for thirty years in books on motoring and motorcycling, new, secondhand and out-of-print. There are thousands of motoring magazines and a good selection of workshop manuals, plus a very efficient mail order system which operates worldwide. Any book which is not on their shelves can be back-ordered and quoted when in stock. They are keen buyers of motoring books.

Osterley

OSTERLEY BOOKSHOP
168a Thornbury Road, Osterley,
Middx., TW7 4QE.   **081-560 6206**

Subjects: General secondhand.
Hours: Mon - Sun 10.00 - 5.30.

Housed in a disused railway station on the Piccadilly Line, this secondhand bookshop faces the main entrance to Osterley House, a National Trust property. The subjects are arranged by sections and, where possible, by author. There is a large selection of stock which is changed weekly with new books being added every Monday.

Kingston-upon-Thames

WATERSTONE'S BOOKSELLERS
23-25 Thames Street, Kingston upon Thames,
Surrey, KT1 1PH.   **081-547 1221**

Subjects: General.
Hours: Mon - Fri 9.30 - 10.00. Sat 9.30 - 7.00. Sun
12.00 - 7.00.
Services: Special orders, mail order, school and library supply,
out-of-print book search, credit cards.

Two large floors comprise this branch of Waterstone's in the heart
of Kingston's shopping precinct. A wide range of general interests
are catered for, and there is a well-rounded selection of fiction,
history, gardening and biography titles. The staff in all departments
are knowledgeable and maintain the stock themselves.

W.H. SMITH LTD.
11-13 Thames Street, Kingston upon Thames,
Surrey, KT1 1PQ.   **081-549 7631**

Subjects: General.
Hours: Mon - Sat 8.30 - 5.30. Tue 9.30 - 5.30.
Services: Special orders, credit cards.

The book department of this branch of W.H.Smith is on the first
floor with the travel agency and recorded music. A large area is
devoted to the books and there is a very wide range of general
subjects in both hardback and paperback. The use of a lift is
available on request.

VOLUME I BOOKSHOP
**107 Clarence Street, Kingston upon Thames,
Surrey, KT1 1QT**   081-541 5481

Subjects: General.
Hours: Mon - Sat 9.00 - 6.00.
Services: Special orders, credit cards.

A general bookshop stocking both paperbacks and hardbacks.
There is a comprehensive range of paperback fiction from many of
the major publishers, a selection of books of popular general
interest such as cookery, gardening and travel, and a children's
section.

HAMMICK'S BOOKSTORE
**2 Church Street, Kingston upon Thames,
Surrey, KT1 1RJ.**   081-541 5411

Subjects: General, children's.
Hours: Mon - Sat 9.00 - 5.30. Thu 9.00 - 8.00.
Services: Special orders, mail order, credit cards.

A bright and cheerful general bookshop offering approximately
15,000 titles, this branch of Hammick's is near the ancient Apple
Market. There is a well designed children's section which is soon to
be extended. Other products include maps, greetings cards and
talking books. Customer orders are welcomed and many can be
supplied within forty-eight hours.

BOOTS THE CHEMIST
**42 Union Street, Kingston upon Thames,
Surrey, KT1 1RP.**   081-541 1644

Subjects: General, bargain books.
Hours: Mon - Wed 9.00 - 5.30. Thu 9.00 - 8.00. Fri, Sat 9.00
               - 6.00.
Services: Credit cards.

One of four Boots the Chemist branches in Greater London with a
book department. The books are on the first floor next to the toy
department and the stock consists mainly of light fiction and
popular general subjects. Bestsellers and new titles are displayed.
Bargain books are also stocked.

BENTALLS LTD.
Kingston upon Thames, Surrey, KT1 1TX.　　　　**081-546 1001**

Subjects: General, children's.
Hours: Mon - Sat 9.00 - 5.30. Thu 9.00 - 9.00.
Services: Special orders, credit cards.

Bentalls' book department is on the ground floor near the Fife Road entrance to the store. The paperback fiction section caters for a wide range of tastes and there are stands for bestsellers and new titles. General sections include cookery, gardening, sports, the arts, natural history, travel, health, BBC publications, reference books and dictionaries. The separate children's corner is well stocked.

HATCHARDS
2 Brook Street, Kingston upon Thames,
Surrey, KT1 2HA.　　　　**081-546 7592**

Subjects: General, academic.
Hours: Mon - Sat 9.00 - 5.30. Tue 9.30 - 5.30.
Services: Special orders, mail order, institutional supply, school supply, out-of-print book search, credit cards.

A general bookshop which also caters particularly for local students but has a general range of academic books. (Formerly Botes Bookshop.)

THE SMOKEBOX
3 Cromwell Road, Kingston upon Thames,
Surrey, KT2 6RF.　　　　**081-549 9700**

Subjects: Railways, shipping, buses, trams, aircraft.
Hours: Tue - Sat 10.30 - 6.00.
Services: Books bought.

A small specialist bookshop packed with books and magazines for the transport enthusiast. The largely secondhand stock covers a wide variety of subjects in the areas of transport represented and is sought after by a clientele which is worldwide. The owner is interested in buying books in his specialist field.

DERRICK NIGHTINGALE
32 Coombe Road, Kingston upon Thames,
Surrey, KT2 7AG.   **081-549 5144**

Subjects: Secondhand, antiquarian.
Hours: Mon - Sat 9.00 - 1.00. 2.00 - 5.00. Wed 9.00 - 1.00.

A small shop with a medium stock of secondhand and antiquarian
books covering a wide range of subjects.

New Malden

CANNINGS
181 High Street, New Malden, Surrey, KT3 4BL.   **081-942 0450**

Subjects: General.
Hours: Mon - Sat 9.00 - 5.30.
Services: Special orders, school and library suppliers.

Cannings has been run as a family business since it opened in 1935
in a converted Victorian house which had its own lending library.
The book department has since been extended to three times the size
of the original building. They are a major supplier of textbooks to
libraries and schools.

W.H. SMITH LTD.
112 High Street, New Malden, Surrey, KT3 4FU.   **081-949 5907**

Subjects: General.
Hours: Mon - Sat 8.30 - 5.30.
Services: Special orders, credit cards.

A long, narrow shop half-way down the High Street. It is one of
the smaller branches of W.H. Smith with the usual general range of
books in hardback and paperback.

Surbiton

REGENCY BOOK SHOP
45 Victoria Road, Surbiton, Surrey, KT6 4JL.   **081-399 2188**

Subjects: General.
Hours: Mon - Sat 9.00 - 5.30.
Services: Special orders.

The small and welcoming Regency Book Shop is unique in Surbiton in offering all the facilities of a comprehensive, well-displayed stock to buy or to browse through and the bonus of a helpful, well-informed staff. Their ordering service attempts to meet any customer request, however small or specialised.

HIGHWAY BOOKS LTD.
277 Ewell Road, Surbiton, Surrey, KT6 7AB.   **081-399 8363**

Subjects: Religious (adults' and children's), R.E. teaching, secondhand theology and religious.
Hours: Mon - Sat 9.00 - 5.30.
Services: Special orders, photocopying, school suppliers.

This bookshop specialises mainly in the Christian faith with other religions represented on a much smaller scale. Music cassettes and cards are available. On the same premises 'The Book Addict' operates as a general library and school supplier.

Ilford

BOOTS THE CHEMIST
177-185 High Road, Ilford, Essex, IG1 1DE.   081-533 2116/7/8

Subjects: General.
Hours: Mon - Sat 9.00 - 5.30.
Services: Credit cards.

This branch of Boots The Chemist has a small book department on the lower ground floor. There is a range of popular general interest books and light fiction in stock. Bargain books, new titles and paperback bestsellers are displayed and there is a stand of Boots' own publications.

W.H. SMITH LTD.
151-153 High Road, Ilford, Essex, IG1 1DQ.   081-478 6251

Subjects: General.
Hours: Mon - Sat 8.30 - 5.30. Tue 9.30 - 5.30.
Services: Special orders, credit cards.

Opposite the Town Hall in a pedestrian-only part of the High Road, this W.H. Smith has a general range of books in paperback and hardback.

EDWARD TERRY BOOKSELLER
26 Chapel Road, Ilford, Essex, IG1 2AH.   081-478 2850

Subjects: General secondhand.
Hours: Mon - Sat 10.00 - 4.00. Closed Thu.

Previously of 6 Roden Street, this secondhand bookshop has a stock of about ten thousand books.

OWEN CLARK & CO. LTD.
129-133 Cranbrook Road, Ilford,
Essex, IG1 4QB.   **081-478 0324/7071**

Subjects: General, academic, art, Open University (all courses).
Hours: Mon - Sat 9.00 - 5.30.
Services: Mail order, special orders, school and educational supply, credit cards.

A retail store with a good selection of general paperback and hardback books. They provide a prompt service to educational establishments, take customers' orders and are Open University stockists. The main part of their business consists of commercial stationery and office products coupled with art and graphic materials and drawing office equipment. Art books are, therefore, well represented.

Woodford Green

THE VILLAGE BOOKSHOP
475 High Road, Woodford Green, Essex IG8 0XE. 081-506 0551

Subjects: General, children's.
Hours: Mon - Fri 9.00 - 5.30. Sat 9.30 - 5.30.
Services: Post-a-book, special orders, credit cards.

On the borders of Epping Forest, there is very much a village atmosphere in this small but well-stocked bookshop. The staff are friendly and helpful and are proud of their fast order service.

Borough of Richmond

Hampton

IAN SHERIDAN'S BOOKSHOP
Thames Villa, 34 Thame Street,
Hampton, Middlesex, TW12 2DX.   **081-979 1704**

Subjects: General, antiquarian and secondhand.
Hours: Mon - Sun 10.00 - 7.00.

A Victorian bookshop one mile up river from Hampton Court Palace in the village of Hampton-upon-Thames. Open seven days a week.

Kew

THE KEW SHOP
Royal Botanic Gardens, Kew,
Richmond, Surrey, TW9 3AB.   **081-940 1171**

Subjects: Gardens and gardening, botany, natural history, conservation.
Hours: Mon - Sun 10.00 - 5.30 (Summer). Mon - Sun 10.00 - 3.30 (Winter).
Services: Catalogue, credit cards.

Located near the Orangery near the main gate, The Kew Shop has an interesting range of books on gardens and gardening, natural history and related subjects. There are high illustrated, glossy books on the gardens of stately homes; academic publications on flora from around the world; books on various forms of wildlife including insects and birds; books on conservation, botanical art and how to draw and paint from nature; the works of natural historians and many other subjects.

LLOYD'S OF KEW
9 Mortlake Terrace, Kew,
Richmond, Surrey, TW9 3DT.   **081-940 2512**

Subjects: Gardening, botany, some general (secondhand).
Hours: Mon - Sat 10.00 - 5.30. Closed Wed.
Services: Mail order, catalogue, search service, credit cards.

Established thirty-five years ago, Lloyd's of Kew has the largest stock of old and out-of-print gardening books in the United Kingdom. Their comprehensive catalogue on this subject, issued in late October, lists over two thousand titles and is circulated worldwide. There is a free search service for scarce books which you are not obliged to buy if they are tracked down.

THE KEW BOOKSHOP
1-2 Station Approach, Kew,
Richmond, Surrey, TW9 3QB.   **081-940 0030**

Subjects: General.
Hours: Mon - Sat 9.30 - 6.00 (flexible).
Services: Special orders, credit cards.

Newly opened in 1989, the Kew Bookshop is a small general bookshop in the station forecourt right in the heart of Kew. The stock covers most subjects including fiction, biography, cookery, gardening, the environment, etc.. There is a good children's section; also maps, cards and giftwrap.

Richmond

THEY WALK AMONG US
30 Union Court, Sheen Road,
Richmond, Surrey, TW9 1AA.   **081-948 8476**

Subjects: Comics, graphic novels, science-fiction, music biographies (new and secondhand).
Hours: Mon - Fri 9.30 - 5.30. Sat 9.30 - 6.00.
Services: Mail order (catalogue), back issue catalogue, free search service for comics, standing orders.

Recently opened, this comic shop with an intriguing name specialises in American, Japanese (translations), European and British comics, graphic novels including Tintin and Asterix, science-fiction, music biographies and a small line of portfolios by popular fantasy artists. The stock is both new and secondhand and includes old British annuals. Related merchandise such as T-shirts, posters and magazines and a limited range of fantasy role-playing games are also stocked. Weekend events will include signings of their work by artists and writers.

SCRIPTURE UNION BOOKSHOP
14 Eton Street, Richmond, Surrey, TW9 1EE.   **081-940 2915**

Subjects: Christian books.
Hours: Mon - Sat 9.00 - 5.30.
Services: Special orders, church bookstalls, video hire, free delivery of bulk orders.

The shop was refurbished in 1989 and there is now more room to look around in comfort. The improved music section carries cassettes and compact discs, and the children's department upstairs is an added attraction which pleases harrassed parents. It is only two minutes' walk away from car parks and the town centre and five minutes from Richmond British Rail/tube station.

ALEC THORNE
**9 Brewers Lane, Richmond,
Surrey, TW9 1HH.**   **081-948 1665**

Subjects: Antiquarian books, maps and prints.
Hours: Mon - Sat 9.30 - 5.30.
Services: Catalogues, book search, credit cards.

A compact and slightly ramshackle shop, nearly three hundred and fifty years old which is located in a narrow pedestrian walkway and surrounded by antique shops. The select stock of antiquarian, books, maps and prints is of a high quality. The atmosphere is informal and friendly.

HATCHARDS
**1-3 Lower George Street, Richmond,
Surrey, TW9 1HU.**   **081-948 7181**

Subjects: General, children's, children's educational, business.
Hours: Mon - Sat 9.00 - 5.30. Tue 9.30 - 5.30.
Services: Special orders, post-a-book, search service, catalogue, credit cards.

Reopened after a major refit in June 1989, this branch of Hatchards is strong on art, drama, poetry, business, education to A-level standard and children's books. Their recently established children's Hodgeheg Club is proving very popular. There is a wide range of books in all general subjects.

W. & A. HOUBEN
2 Church Court, Richmond, Surrey, TW9 1JL.   **081-940 1055**

Subjects: General, new and secondhand, academic.
Hours: Mon - Sat 10.00 - 6.00.
Services: Special orders, mail order, credit cards.

A good general/academic bookshop in a pedestrian way off George Street (beside Owen & Owen). Extensive stocks of textbooks in the arts and humanities and a thriving secondhand department in the basement. There is a selection of original prints of London and the local area.

W.H. SMITH LTD.
16-17 George Street, Richmond,
Surrey, TW9 1JS.   **081-940 3671**

Subjects: General.
Hours: Mon - Fri 8.45 - 5.30. Tue 9.30 - 5.30. Sat 9.00 - 6.00.
Services: Special orders, credit cards.

A large W.H. Smith with a correspondingly large range of books in general subjects, including some text-books and reference books. Bestsellers in hardback and paperback are near the front of the shop.

THE OPEN BOOK
10 King Street, Richmond,
Surrey, TW9 1ND.   **081-940 1802**

Subjects: General.
Hours: Mon - Fri 9.30 - 6.00. Sat 9.30 - 7.00.
Services: Book search, local delivery, mail order, credit cards.

A well-stocked general bookshop whose owner has had many years' experience in publishing. Literature, including texts in foreign languages, poetry, biography and travel are all strong sections. Hanging baskets of plants and additional illumination from a central skylight help to make this a pleasant place in which to browse.

THE LION & UNICORN BOOKSHOP
19 King Street, Richmond,
Surrey, TW9 1ND.
081-940 0483

Subjects: Children's, spoken word cassettes.
Hours: Mon - Sat 9.30 - 5.30.
Services: Special orders, school orders, exhibitions organised, school bookshop supplier, author visits.

The Lion & Unicorn is one of the very few specialist children's bookshops in the country. It has a bright and friendly atmosphere in which children and parents alike can relax. A popular feature of the shop is the play table, well-stocked with books, jigsaws and building bricks, where young children are safely occupied while their parents look around in peace. There is a comprehensive range of carefully selected fiction and non-fiction in hardback and paperback and helpful, experienced staff on hand to give advice or information.

THE RICHMOND BOOKSHOP
20 Red Lion Street, Richmond,
Surrey, TW9 1RW.
081-940 5512

Subjects: General secondhand, mainly 20th century.
Hours: Fri, Sat 9.30 - 6.00. (Last orders 5.55).

16,000 books tower nine shelves high, making a good head for heights desirable. The slightly restricted opening hours give ample scope for the proprietors' scavenging instincts. The stock not only changes but moves constantly, as they rotate the alphabet within each section, so that all books bask at eye-level every few weeks. There is a strong emphasis on the arts and humanities, reflecting the enthusiasms of the owner. The main sections are history, literary criticism, art, fiction, travel, poetry, military, natural history, biography, psychology, music and theatre. Current review copies are a lure for many regulars. Saturdays tend to be somewhat turbulent; if you prefer peaceful browsing, try Friday.

W.H.SMITH LTD.
Station Bookshop, Richmond,
Surrey, TW9 2NA.   **081-940 0993**

Subjects: Paperback fiction, bargain books.
Hours: Mon - Fri 6.00 a.m. - 7.00 p.m. Sat 7.00 - 5.00. Sun 9.00
            - 2.00.
Services: Credit cards.

Inside the main entrance to the railway station, this W.H. Smith
station bookshop carries the bestsellers in paperback and a small
selection of paperback fiction as well as bargain books and London
guides and maps. The railway traveller will also be able to purchase
newspapers, magazines, cards, stationery and confectionery here.

WATERSTONE'S BOOKSELLERS
2-6 Hill Street, Richmond,
Surrey, TW10 6UA.   **081-332 1600**

Subjects: General
Hours: Mon - Fri 9.30 - 9.00. Sat 9.30 - 7.00. Sun 12.00 - 7.00.
Services: Special orders, mail order, school and library supply,
            out-of-print book search, credit cards.

Three large floors comprise this branch of Waterstone's which is on
a corner site in the heart of Richmond's shopping district. A wide
range of general interests are catered for, and there is also an
extensive selection of fiction, history, gardening, biography and
women's studies titles. The staff in all departments are
knowledgeable and maintain the stock themselves.

BALDUR BOOKSHOP
44 Hill Rise, Richmond,
Surrey, TW10 6UB.   **081-940 1214**

Subjects: General, English literature, cricket, (secondhand).
Hours: Mon - Sat 10.00 - 5.00. Closed Wed.

This bookshop has had one proprietor since 1933. English literature
and cricket are specialities. There are also postcards and a modest
selection of prints.

Teddington

THE SWAN BOOKSHOP
12 Church Road, Teddington, Middx., TW11 8PB. 081-977 8920

Subjects: General, reference, maps, children's.
Hours: Mon - Fri 9.00 - 5.30. Wed 9.00 - 1.00. Sat 9.00 - 5.00.
Services: Special orders, credit cards.

Run by a husband and wife team with over forty years' experience of bookselling between them, this small general bookshop aims to stock the major reviewed titles in hardback and paperback and holds a good general back stock, mainly in paperback. There is a strong reference section with the Children's Britannica and Macmillan Family Encyclopaedia held in stock. Their map section includes the full range of the Landranger, Outdoor Leisure and Tourist Ordnance Survey maps. There is a separate children's section.

Twickenham

OPEN BOOKS
West London Institute of Higher Education,
Gordon House, 300 St. Margaret's Road,
Twickenham, Middx., TW1 1PT.   **081-891 0121**

Subjects: Education, social sciences, general secondhand.
Hours: Mon - Fri 11.00 - 2.00. 3.00 - 4.30 (termtime only).

This is a campus bookshop catering for the needs of the students but open to the public. There is a large general selection of secondhand books.

LANGTON'S BOOKSHOP
44/45 Church Street, Twickenham,
Middx., TW1 3NT.   **081-892 3800**

Subjects: General, children's.
Hours: Mon - Sat 9.30 - 5.30.
Services: Special orders, credit cards, search service.

Family-owned, this is in an attractive, early eighteenth century shop with a well designed modern extension. The 'olde worlde' appearance is belied by the computerised stock control and Whitakers on CDRom. They offer a wide selection of books and maps.

ST. MARY'S COLLEGE BOOKSHOP
St. Mary's College, Waldegrave Road,
Strawberry Hill, Twickenham, Middx., TW1 4SX.   081-891 4255

Subjects: Education, academic texts.
Hours: Mon - Fri 9.00 - 5.00 (term time only).
Services: Special orders.

This college bookshop stocks books required for the various courses. The college's main strength is its teacher-training courses but there are also some B.A. and B.Sc. courses not related to teaching. Stationery items are also available. People from outside the college are welcome to use the bookshop.

ANTHONY C. HALL
30 Staines Road, Twickenham, Middx., TW2 5AH. 081-898 2638

Subjects: General secondhand.
Hours: Mon - Fri 9.00 - 5.30. Early closing Wed.
Services: Viewing of specialised stock by arrangement.

In addition to their small general stock, there is a very large specialised stock on Russian and East European studies, the Middle East, Africa, Asia and industrial history, which can be viewed by arrangement.

MARION PITMAN
29 Hampton Road, Twickenham,
Middx., TW2 5QE.   081-898 7165

Subjects: General secondhand.
Hours: Tue, Thu, Sat 1.00 - 6.00. (or by appointment).
Services: Mail order, occasional lists.

A general secondhand bookshop overflowing with books, both fiction and non-fiction, ephemera and bric-a-brac. Good for those who enjoy rummaging.

RITA SHENTON
128 Percy Road, Twickenham, Middx., TW2 6JG. 081-894 6888

Subjects:	Clocks, watches, sundials, bells, workshop techniques (new, secondhand, antiquarian).
Hours:	Longer than 9.00 - 5.00 weekdays but variable. Advantageous to telephone before calling.
Services:	Books bought, search services, international mail order, catalogue, valuations for probate etc.

One of the largest specialist horological booksellers in the country, carrying a full range of in-print titles from British and overseas publishing houses. Remainders and secondhand copies are stocked when available as well as many out-of-print and antiquarian books. Callers are welcome but they would prefer some warning as the office premises are small. They are proud of their reputation for providing an efficient and speedy mail order service. A large, descriptive catalogue is issued annually and they are always willing to offer advice and further information on specific titles.

OPEN BOOKS
Richmond upon Thames College,
Egerton Road, Twickenham, Middx., TW2 7SJ.   081-892 6656

Subjects:	A-level textbooks, course books.
Hours:	Mon - Fri 10.00 - 2.00 (termtime only).

A campus bookshop catering for the needs of the students but open to the public. It stocks mainly A-level textbooks and stationery.

Belmont

CHEAM BOOK SHOP
32 Station Road, Belmont, Sutton,
Surrey, SM2 6BS.   **081-642 1234**

Subjects: General secondhand.
Hours: Mon - Sat 9.00 - 5.00. Closed Wed.

The very large stock of books occupies nine rooms, four of them in the garden. Most subjects and fiction are stocked, both secondhand and rare. There are pictures and prints and some interesting bric-a-brac in the window. Browsing here in Belmont can be useful and satisfying.

Cheam

THE BROADWAY BOOKSHOP
51 The Broadway, Cheam, Surrey, SM3 8BL.   **081-643 7048**

Subjects: General.
Hours: Mon - Sat 9.30 - 5.30.
Services: Special orders, credit cards.

A small bookshop fitting neatly into a converted sixteenth century cottage. It caters particularly for customers who like individual attention. The owners and staff take great pride in the special order service, which supplements the wider general stock.

WHITEHALL BOOKSHOP
43 The Broadway, Cheam, Surrey, SM3 8BL.   **081-643 8272**

Subjects: General secondhand and antiquarian.
Hours: Mon - Sat 9.30 - 5.30.

A long bookshop with space to look around. It has quite a rapid turnover of stock and not all of it is on display. There is some specialisation in topography and sport and, when available, military subjects.

W.H. SMITH LTD.
4 Station Way, Cheam, Surrey, SM3 8SW.   **081-643 5848**

Subjects: General.
Hours: Mon - Sat 8.30 - 5.30.
Services: Special orders, credit cards.

Situated at the traffic lights near the centre of Cheam, this W.H. Smith store stocks a fairly small general range of books.

Sutton

CROWNBOOKS LTD.
5 Grove Road, Sutton, Surrey, SM1 1BB.   **081-642 6511**

Subjects: Christian literature.
Hours: Mon - Sat 9.00 - 5.30.

Close to the Post Office off Sutton High Street, this Christian family bookshop caters for all ages with Christian books, music cassettes, videos and cards on offer.

BAINES BOOKSHOP
3 Lower Square, Civic Centre,
Sutton, Surrey, SM1 1EA.   **081-661 1677**

Subjects: General.
Hours: Mon - Sat 9.00 - 5.30.
Services: Special orders, credit cards.

A well-stocked general bookshop in a pedestrian-only square which is overlooked by the Central Library. Its subject range includes history, psychology, biography, art and fiction.

HAMMICK'S BOOKSTORE
13 Times 2, Sutton, Surrey, SM1 1LF.   **081-642 6842**

Subjects: General.
Hours: Mon - Sat 9.00 - 5.30.
Services: Special orders, credit cards.

A pleasant, friendly bookshop offering approximately 15,000 titles and including a special area for children's books. Other products sold include maps, greetings cards and talking books. Customer orders are welcomed and many can be supplied within forty-eight hours.

W.H. SMITH LTD.
118 High Street, Sutton, Surrey, SM1 1LU.   **081-643 4512**

Subjects: General.
Hours: Mon - Sat 8.30 - 5.30.
Services: Special orders, post-a-book, credit cards.

A spacious W.H.Smith on two floors with the books on the upper floor. There is a large paperback fiction section and the usual general range in hardback and paperback. The children's section has a good selection of both fiction and education books. Pedestrian access only to this part of the High Street after 10 a.m.

Wallington

W.H. SMITH LTD.
92 Woodcote Road, Wallington, Surrey, SM6 0NG. 081-669 7739

Subjects: General.
Hours: Mon - Sat 8.30 - 5.30.
Services: Special orders, credit cards.

This W.H. Smith occupies two long rooms adjacent to each other and linked by a doorway. In one there is a middling-sized range of books on a variety of subjects, including fiction, in hardback and paperback, also newspapers and magazines; in the other stationery, cards and recorded music.

THE OASIS CHRISTIAN CENTRE
23 Wallington Square, Wallington,
Surrey, SM6 8RG.   **081-773 1428**

Subjects: Christian literature.
Hours: Mon - Sat 9.00 - 5.30. Wed 9.30 - 1.30.
Services: Special orders - any Christian book.

A well-stocked shop which also specialises in relevant music cassettes and compact discs, greetings and special occasion cards, and craft items. There is a coffee bar where you may relax after shopping.

Worcester Park

W.H. SMITH LTD.
153 Central Road, Worcester Park,
Surrey, KT4 8DT.   **081-337 1945**

Subjects: General.
Hours: Mon - Fri 8.45 - 5.30. Sat 8.30 - 5.30.
Services: Special orders, credit cards.

This W.H.Smith carries a general range of books in hardback and
paperback including fiction and children's books.

Shop Index

Subject Index

Most branches of some of the major bookshops appear rarely, if at all, in this index. Dillons, Foyles, Hatchards, Waterstones, Sherratt & Hughes and Books Etc are notable examples.

This is because they are truly general bookshops carrying good ranges of books on a great many subjects, yet specialising in none. There are other general bookshops — not on the same scale perhaps, but nevertheless carrying creditable ranges — which, for the same reason, we have not included in this index.

Hence when looking for a particular book or type of book, one should consider whether it may be available at a general bookshop or only at a specialist bookshop. If the former, a search of our listings in a convenient postal district would seem the easiest way of deciding where to go; if the latter, then the subject index should prove helpful.